TEACHER'S GUIDE
Every Student Learns

D1517123

Science

PEARSON
Scott Foresman

Editorial Offices: Glenview, Illinois • Parsippany, New Jersey • New York, New York
Sales Offices: Needham, Massachusetts • Duluth, Georgia • Glenview, Illinois
Coppell, Texas • Sacramento, California • Mesa, Arizona

www.sfsuccessnet.com

Series Authors

Dr. Timothy Cooney
Professor of Earth Science and Science Education
University of Northern Iowa (UNI)
Cedar Falls, Iowa

Dr. Jim Cummins
Professor
Department of Curriculum, Teaching, and Learning
The University of Toronto
Toronto, Canada

Dr. James Flood
Distinguished Professor of Literacy and Language
School of Teacher Education
San Diego State University
San Diego, California

Barbara Kay Foots, M.Ed.
Science Education Consultant
Houston, Texas

Dr. M. Jenice Goldston
Associate Professor of Science Education
Department of Elementary Education Programs
University of Alabama
Tuscaloosa, Alabama

Dr. Shirley Gholston Key
Associate Professor of Science Education
Instruction and Curriculum Leadership Department
College of Education
University of Memphis
Memphis, Tennessee

Dr. Diane Lapp
Distinguished Professor of Reading and Language Arts in Teacher Education
San Diego State University
San Diego, California

Sheryl A. Mercier
Classroom Teacher
Dunlap Elementary School
Dunlap, California

Dr. Karen L. Ostlund
UTeach, College of Natural Sciences
The University of Texas at Austin
Austin, Texas

Dr. Nancy Romance
Professor of Science Education & Principal Investigator
NSF/IERI Science IDEAS Project
Charles E. Schmidt College of Science
Florida Atlantic University
Boca Raton, Florida

Dr. William Tate
Chair and Professor of Education and Applied Statistics
Department of Education
Washington University
St. Louis, Missouri

Dr. Kathryn C. Thornton
Professor
School of Engineering and Applied Science
University of Virginia
Charlottesville, Virginia

Dr. Leon Ukens
Professor of Science Education
Department of Physics, Astronomy, and Geosciences
Towson University
Towson, Maryland

Steve Weinberg
Consultant
Connecticut Center for Advanced Technology
East Hartford, Connecticut

Consulting Author

Dr. Michael P. Klentschy
Superintendent
El Centro Elementary School District
El Centro, California

ISBN: 0-328-14568-8

© Pearson Education, Inc. **2**

Unit A
Life Science

Unit B
Earth Science

Unit C
Physical Science

Unit D
Space and Technology

Overview

Every Student Learns Teacher's Guide is a lesson-by-lesson companion to Scott Foresman *Science*. It has been designed to provide manageable support for teachers and their students who are challenged by language issues in science, no matter what the first language may be.

Every Student Learns Teacher's Guide is built upon the three pillars of English language learning as identified by Dr. Jim Cummins of the University of Toronto.

- Activate Prior Knowledge/Build Background Knowledge
- Access Content
- Extend Language

Read more about how to use the three pillars to support ESL students in learning the language of science on the following pages.

For every chapter, the **Picture It!** page is a blackline master to use with the How to Read Science page in the Student Edition. Help students use these masters to practice using target reading skills as they read. Each master provides guided practice using a picture or graphic organizer with text. Teaching notes and answers can be found on the page that follows it (Lesson 1 of the chapter).

For every lesson in each chapter, teaching strategies are provided using the three pillars, with scripted direct instruction highlighted in bold type.

- **Activate Prior Knowledge/Build Background Knowledge**
  Suggestions are provided to help you relate science concepts and vocabulary to students' experiences using strategies such as brainstorming, discussion, and demonstrations with concrete examples or visual aids (Picture/Text Walk).

- **Access Content** Discussion suggestions are provided in **Picture/Text Walk** to help students use context and picture clues, referring to pictures in the Student Edition.

- **Extend Language** A variety of strategies are provided to help students develop language skills and proficiency in academic language.

You may choose to use any or all of these suggestions and strategies as needed. **Every Student Learns Teacher's Guide** is a flexible tool that will work in a wide range of classrooms. Use these pages in conjunction with the ESL support notes throughout your Teacher's Edition to provide complete support for your second language learners.

Supporting ESL Students in Learning the Language of Science

Dr. Jim Cummins, Professor
Department of Curriculum, Teaching, and Learning
The University of Toronto
Toronto, Canada

Because language is infused into all aspects of the teaching of science, students whose knowledge of English is limited are likely to have difficulty accessing scientific concepts and expressing their understanding of these concepts in oral and written language. Therefore, teachers are faced with the challenge of modifying their instruction in ways that will assist ESL students.

Effective academic language instruction for ESL students across the curriculum is built on three fundamental pillars:

1. Activate Prior Knowledge/Build Background Knowledge
2. Access Content
3. Extend Language

In developing scientific knowledge through language, and language abilities through science, we can apply these three instructional principles in powerful ways.

1. Activate Prior Knowledge/Build Background Knowledge

Prior knowledge is the foundation of learning. When students read a scientific text, they construct meaning by bringing their prior knowledge of language, science, and of the world in general to the text. Students may not explicitly realize what they know about a particular topic or issue. Activating their prior knowledge brings it to consciousness and facilitates learning.

Activating prior knowledge and building background knowledge are important for all students, but particularly for ESL students who may be struggling with unfamiliar vocabulary and grammatical structures in addition to complex new concepts. Building this context permits students to understand more complex language and to pursue more cognitively demanding activities. It lessens the cognitive load of the text and frees up brain power.

Activation of prior knowledge enables teachers to validate ESL students' background experiences and affirm their cultural knowledge. Inviting students to contribute what they already know to the class discussion communicates to students that the cultural and linguistic knowledge they are bringing into the classroom is valuable.

Strategies for activating prior knowledge and building background knowledge.

A variety of strategies to activate students' prior knowledge are embedded in Scott Foresman *Science*.

- *Brainstorming/Discussion* This type of language interaction can happen in the context of a whole class, in small groups, or in pairs; for example, students can interview a partner to find out what each one knows about a particular topic. Discussion can also be highly effective in making abstract concepts more concrete and comprehensible.
- *Use of graphic organizers* These can be used to capture the results of brainstorming and discussion. K-W-L- charts, word webs, and many other graphic organizers enable students to record and organize their information.
- *Visuals in texts* Photographs, charts, and graphs can be used to stimulate discussion about aspects of what is depicted and to encourage students to predict what the text is likely to be about.
- *Short-term direct experiences* Quick activities and questions about students' experiences provide opportunities for students to observe science-related phenomena and can stimulate discussion of what students have observed. Teachers help students relate their observations or experiences to the content of the science lesson.
- *Long-term direct experiences* Class projects and formal inquiry activities provide opportunities for students to deepen their knowledge of abstract concepts.
- *Writing about what we know* Dialogue journals for note taking and responses to written prompts are useful means for the student to both record information and review it later.

2. Access Content

We can also support or *scaffold* students' learning by modifying the input itself. We provide this scaffolding by embedding the content in a richly redundant context with multiple routes to the meaning in addition to the language itself. Building this redundancy enables ESL students to access the content despite any limitations in English language proficiency.

Strategies that improve student access to academic content.

The following methods, which you will find embedded in Scott Foresman *Science*, can help students more effectively get access to meaning.

- *Use Visuals* Visuals enable students to "see" the basic concept we are trying to teach much more effectively than if we rely only on words. When students are reading science textbooks, we can systematically draw their attention to the importance of context and picture clues in figuring out the meaning. The Picture/Text Walk feature in Scott Foresman *Science* Every Student Learns Teacher's Guide draws attention to specific pictures and offers models of language the teacher can use to talk about those pictures with the students to clarify the meaning.

© Pearson Education, Inc. 2

- ***Dramatize/Act Out*** For beginning ESL students, *Total Physical Response,* where students physically represent a phenomenon or act out commands, can be highly effective.
- ***Clarify Language*** Language-oriented activities aim to clarify the meanings of new words and concepts. Teachers can modify their language by paraphrasing ideas and explaining new concepts and words. They explain new words by providing synonyms, antonyms, and definitions either in English or in the home language of students. Important vocabulary can be repeated and recycled as part of the paraphrasing of ideas. The meaning can also be communicated and/or reinforced through gestures, body language, and demonstrations.
- ***Make Personal and Cultural Connections*** Scripted questions in the Scott Foresman *Science* Every Student Learns Teacher's Guide suggest ways to link content to students' everyday experiences. These content connections validate students' sense of identity and make the learning more meaningful.
- ***Make Cross-Curricular Connections*** The more cognitive operations students perform related to a particular issue or problem, the deeper their comprehension becomes.
- ***Provide Hands-on Experiences*** The more we can contextualize or personalize abstract concepts by embedding them in students' hands-on experiences, the more comprehensible they will become for students. Hands-on projects also allow students to link the conversational language they use in the "real" world and the more abstract and specialized language they are learning in science. Discussions about concrete phenomena and problems demystify the language of science. The abstract concepts we learn in science help us understand what we see with our very own eyes and vice-versa.
- ***Encourage Learning Strategies*** Learning strategies are useful for all students, but particularly for ESL students who face obvious challenges in accessing curricular content. Examples of strategies included in Scott Foresman *Science* are: planning tasks or activities, visualization, grouping and classifying information, taking notes and summarizing information, questioning for clarification, and using multiple resources and reference materials to find information or complete a task.

3. Extend Language

A systematic focus on and exploration of language is essential if students are to develop knowledge of the specific vocabulary and text structures that are used in scientific discourse. Students can systematically collect the meanings of words and phrases they encounter in science texts in a personal or group *language bank.*

Strategies that help students accelerate their acquisition of academic language.

A variety of strategies to extend students' language knowledge and awareness are embedded in Scott Foresman *Science*.

- **Explore Etymology** Paradoxically, the complexity of scientific language provides some important opportunities for language exploration. A large percentage of the less frequent academic and technical vocabulary of English derives from Latin and Greek roots. So word formation often follows some very predictable patterns.

- **Identify Rules and Conventions** When students know some of the rules or conventions of how academic words are formed, they have an edge in extending their vocabulary. It helps them not only figure out the meanings of individual words but also how to form different parts of speech from these words.

- **Relate Academic Words to Students' First Language** This encourages students to relate the English word to their prior knowledge of the word (or related words in their first language). It also provides students with an opportunity to display and feel proud of their first language linguistic expertise.

- **Identify and Practice Conjugates** When we demystify how academic language works, students are more likely to recognize parts of speech in their reading of complex text across the curriculum and to become more adept at inferring meanings from context. For example, the student who recognizes that *acceleration* is a noun (rather than a verb or adjective) has taken a step closer to the meaning of the term in the context of a particular sentence or text.

- **Model Appropriate Academic Language** If teachers provide good models, then students can extend their own command of more formal registers of language. In addition, students must be given the opportunity and incentive to use academic language in both oral and written modalities.

Conclusion

Science will assume relevance to students and be learned much more effectively when students can relate the content of instruction to their prior experience and current interests. In addition to activating students' prior knowledge and building background knowledge, we may need to modify our instruction in specific ways to make the content accessible to ESL students who are still in the process of catching up to native-speakers in academic English language proficiency.

These supports should focus not only on making the scientific content comprehensible to students but also on extending their awareness of how the language of science works. In this way, students can develop insights about academic language that will bear fruit in other areas. When we integrate these active uses of language with the science curriculum, students benefit both with respect to their knowledge of scientific content and language abilities.

References

Chamot, A. U., and J. M. O'Malley. 1994. *The CALLA Handbook: Implementing the Cognitive Academic Language Learning Approach.* Reading, Mass.: Addison-Wesley.

Collier, V. P., and Thomas, W. P. 1999. Making U.S. schools effective for English language learners, Part 1. *TESOL Matters,* 9:4 (August/September), pp. 1 and 6.

Cummins, J. 2001. *Negotiating identities: Education for empowerment in a diverse society. 2nd edition.* Los Angeles: California Association for Bilingual Education.

Diaz-Rico, L., and K. Z. Weed. 2002. *The crosscultural, language, and academic development handbook: A complete K–12 reference guide. 2nd edition.* Boston: Allyn & Bacon.

Gibbons, P. 1991. *Learning to learn in a second language.* Newtown, Australia: Primary English Teaching Association.

Meyer, L. 2000. Barriers to meaningful instruction for English learners. *Theory into Practice, 34*(2), 228–236.

Neuman, S. B. 1999. Books make a difference: A study of access to literacy. *Reading Research Quarterly, 34*(3), 286–311.

Schmitt, N. 2000. *Vocabulary in language teaching.* Cambridge, U. K.: Cambridge University Press.

⊙ Predict

Read the sentences. Write what you think will happen next. Draw a picture that shows what you predict.

This plant needs water to grow. I give it the water it needs. What will happen?

I Know   I Predict

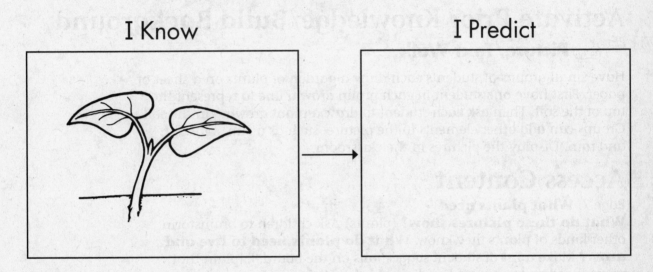

A maple tree has leaves in spring and summer. The tree loses its leaves in cold weather. What will happen in fall and winter?

I Know   I Predict

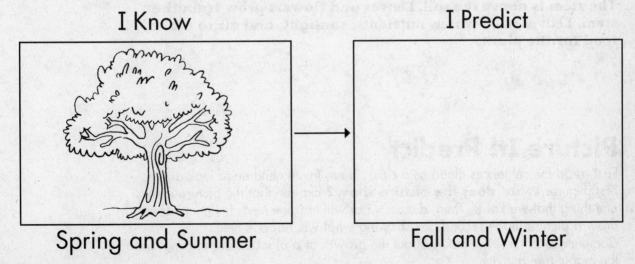

Spring and Summer   Fall and Winter

Lesson 1: What are the parts of a plant?

Vocabulary

*nutrients	soil	*leaves
*roots	*stem	*flower

Activate Prior Knowledge/Build Background

👣👣 Picture/Text Walk

Have small groups of students each draw a garden of plants on a sheet of paper. First have one student in each group draw a line to represent the top of the soil. Then ask each student to draw a plant growing in the soil. Groups can add other elements to the picture, such as a Sun, sunlight, and rain. Display the pictures in the classroom.

Access Content

Page 7: **What plants need**
What do these pictures show? (plants) Ask children to brainstorm other kinds of plants they know. **What do plants need to live and grow?** Make a list of student suggestions on the board. Explain that plants need water, air, and sunlight. **Living things also need *nutrients* to live and grow. Nutrients are in the soil and water.**

Pages 8–9: **The four parts of a plant**
Draw a picture of a plant, including roots and flowers. Label the parts. Point out that there are four main parts of a plant. Ask students to repeat the parts after you: *roots, stem, leaves,* and *flowers.* **Roots are in the soil. The stem is above the soil. Leaves and flowers grow from the stem. Leaves need water, nutrients, sunlight, and air to make food for the plant.**

Picture It! Predict

First, read the sentences aloud as a class. Then, invite children to look at the first picture. **What does the picture show?** Explain that the picture shows one thing that we know. Then, discuss what will happen next. Invite children to draw a picture in the second box showing what will happen next.
Complete the first set of boxes about the growth of a plant before moving on to the maple tree activity.

© Pearson Education, Inc. **2**

Every Student Learns

Lesson 2: How are seeds scattered?

Vocabulary

scatter	protect	fur
spread	travel	burr
fruit	float	

Activate Prior Knowledge/Build Background

Pass around different seeds, including corn kernels, beans, and various flower seeds, or show drawings of seeds. Talk about how a seed grows into a plant. Have students who have planted or seen seeds planted tell what the seeds looked like, how people planted them, and what plants grew from them. Ask students to tell how long it takes for those seeds to grow into plants that make new seeds. Children may also draw the process of a seed growing into a plant.

Access Content

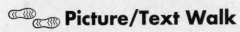 Picture/Text Walk

Pages 10–11: **Seeds and fruits**
Explain that seeds scatter, meaning that they move away from the plant where they grew. Point to the three pictures of fruits with seeds. **These seeds come from different plants.** Explain that fruits cover and protect seeds. Point to the second picture. **What plant is this fruit from? What do the seeds look like?** Then, ask about all three fruits. **Where does each fruit come from? How does each fruit scatter?** If possible, bring in a maple tree fruit and throw it in the air to demonstrate how it spins.

Burrs
Point out that burrs are fruits that hook on to clothing or animal fur. This is how the fruit travels. **Have you gotten a burr on your clothes? Has your pet gotten a burr?** Explain that burrs are like Velcro™. They stick to other things.

Extend Language

Explain that a maple tree fruit *spins* in the air. Explain that *spin* is a verb. Ask students to show how something moves when it spins. Then ask them to show how something moves when it *floats*. Have students say verbs that name different ways that people, animals, and things move. Make a list of these verbs. Ask students to describe the motion of each verb.

Lesson 3: How are plants grouped?

Vocabulary

group	cactus	mosses
fields	cones	ferns

Activate Prior Knowledge/Build Background

Show students pictures of different kinds of flowers growing on plants. Have students brainstorm a list of flowers and the plant each one grows on. Point out that trees are also plants. Ask students to pick a flower from the list and make a drawing of it. Have students show and talk about their drawings in small groups.

Access Content

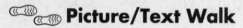 **Picture/Text Walk**

Page 12: **Peach tree**
Explain that there are two main groups of plants. **One kind of plant does not have flowers. The other kind of plant has flowers. What plant is on this page? Does it have flowers?** Point out that the peach tree has flowers. The flowers become fruit that protect the peach seeds inside.

Page 13: **Saguaro cactus**
This plant is a cactus. It grows in the desert. Is this plant in the group that has flowers or the group that doesn't have flowers? Explain that the flowers make seeds. **The seeds fall into the sand. Some of the seeds become new cactus plants.**

Pages 14–15: **Cones, mosses, and ferns**
These plants don't have flowers. Have children point to each plant as you say the name: plants with cones, mosses, and ferns. Explain that some plants have cones. The seeds of these plants grow inside the cones. Explain that some plants, like ferns and mosses, do not make fruits or seeds.

Extend Language

Talk about the word *fruity*. Explain that it comes from the noun *fruit*. To make *fruity*, we add -y to the end of the word. *Fruity* means that something is like fruit or has fruit in it. Have students make adjectives out of the nouns *moss, sugar, water, milk,* and *leaf* and explain the meaning of each one.

Every Student Learns

Lesson 4: How are some woodland plants adapted?

Vocabulary

*environment
*adapted

woodland
needles

Activate Prior Knowledge/Build Background

Pass around photographs of clothes made for hot, warm, cold, and wet weather. Have students explain why people wear these different kinds of clothes. Ask them to talk about what clothes people wear and the kinds of houses they make in different parts of the world. Discuss possible reasons for these differences. Explain that many plants are also adapted or changed to fit what is around them, just like people, clothes, and houses.

Access Content

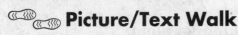 Picture/Text Walk

Pages 16–17: **Two woodlands**
Explain that a plant's *environment* is everything in the place where the plant lives. **What do you see in the pine tree's environment? What do you see in the maple tree's environment?** Explain that pine trees have *adapted*, or changed, so they can live in cold weather. **Do the leaves of a pine tree fall off in the winter? What are its leaves like? What is a maple tree leaf like? Do its leaves fall off in the winter?**

Pages 18–19: **Three woodland plants**
Where do these plants live? What do you see in this environment? Is this environment wet or dry? Explain that the three plants in these pictures are adapted to live in a wet environment. **The cardinal plant has roots that help it live in wet soil. What do you think helps the fanwort live near rivers and streams? How do the sharp hairs on the stinging nettle protect it from animals?**

Lesson 5: How are some prairie plants adapted?

Vocabulary

*prairie	goldenrod
stiff	fuzz

Activate Prior Knowledge/Build Background

Show students the photo of the prairie on pages 20–21. This is a picture of a prairie. **How is this picture different from the forest?** Elicit that there are no trees. **Do you think trees need a lot of water to grow? Do you think the prairie gets a lot of rain?**

Access Content

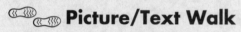 **Picture/Text Walk**

Pages 20–21: **Prairie plants**
What kinds of plants grow on the prairie? What kinds of plants don't grow a lot on the prairie? Explain that on the prairie it can be very hot in the summer and rain very little. Some prairie plants are adapted to keep the water they need. **The goldenrod plant has stiff stems and leaves. They help the plant keep the water it needs to live when it is hot and dry.** Point to the prairie smoke. **What is on the stem and leaves of the prairie smoke plant?** Explain that the fuzz on the prairie smoke helps keep the water the plant needs to live.

Lesson 6: How are some desert plants adapted?

Vocabulary

| desert | direction | sunlight | spines |

Activate Prior Knowledge/Build Background

Show children the photo of the desert on pages 22–23. **Does this look more like a forest or a prairie? Why?**

Access Content

 Picture/Text Walk

Pages 22–23: **Desert plants**
This is a picture of a desert. Many deserts are hot during the day and cool at night. There is very little rain in the desert. Point to the desert almond. **What are the leaves of the desert almond like? Do they grow in one direction or different directions?** Explain that some leaves get less sunlight than other leaves. Those leaves can keep more water for the plant. Point to the saguaro cactus. **Where do you think the saguaro cactus keeps the water it needs to live?** Point to the octopus tree. **Does the octopus tree have long leaves or long spines? How do the long spines help protect the plant from animals?**

Lesson 7: How are some marsh plants adapted?

Vocabulary

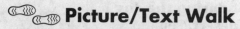

| marsh | insects | trap | digest | sticky |

Activate Prior Knowledge/Build Background

Do you know what an insect is? Name some insects. (flies, ants, bees, beetles) **What animals eat insects? Do you think plants use insects for food? Some plants trap insects. They digest the insects for food.** Tell children that they will learn about some plants that use insects for food.

Access Content

🐾 Picture/Text Walk

Pages 24–25: **Marsh plants**
This is a picture of a marsh. Does a marsh have a little water or a lot of water? Explain that soil in a marsh may not have the nutrients plants need. Explain that cattails are adapted to get the nutrients they need from water in the soil. Point to the picture of the sundew plant. **The sundew plant has sticky hairs on each leaf. What happens when an insect lands on a leaf? Where does the sundew plant get the nutrients it needs?** Explain that a Venus'-flytrap also gets nutrients from insects. **How does a Venus'-flytrap get insects?**

Extend Language

Explain that words sometimes have the names of animals in them. Write *cattail* and show how the word is made up of *cat* and *tail*. Discuss with students why they think people gave the plant that name. Write the words *catfish* and *catnap*. Describe a catfish and a catnap and discuss what each one has to do with cats.

© Pearson Education, Inc. **2**

⊙ Alike and Different

Look at the pictures. Read the paragraph. As you read each sentence, point to the picture clue that matches what you read. Then, look at the chart below.

Cat

Rabbit

Cats have fur. Cats have four legs. Cats have a long tail. Cats have short ears.

Rabbits have fur. Rabbits have four legs. Rabbits have a short tail. Rabbits have long ears.

Alike	Different
Fur	Tail
_____	_____
_____	_____
_____	_____

Lesson 1: What are some animals with backbones?

Vocabulary

*mammals	*reptiles	protect
*birds	*amphibians	
*fish	bones	

Activate Prior Knowledge/Build Background

Tell children to feel down the middle of their backs. **What do you feel?**
Point out to children that they have just felt their backbone. **What do
bones do? What would it be like if you didn't have bones?** Have
children feel their bones in their head, arms, legs, and ribs.

Access Content

Picture/Text Walk

Pages 38–39: **Skunk and deer**
What animals do you see? Have children point to the deer and the
skunk. **How are these animals alike?** Discuss how these animals have
fur and bones. They are mammals. **How are they different?** The deer is
bigger and faster than the skunk. The skunk has a special spray.

Pages 40–41: **Mammals, birds, fish, amphibians, reptiles**
Point to each animal pictured and identify it for the children. **This is a
chipmunk. It is a mammal. This is a hummingbird. It is a bird.
This is a fish. This is an iguana. It is a reptile. This is a frog. It
is an amphibian.** Emphasize that each animal has a backbone. Invite
children to name things that make each animal different.

Extend Language

Explain how to use the indefinite article *an.* Explain that it precedes nouns
that start with a vowel sound. The word *a* precedes words that begin with
a consonant sound. Model how to use these articles with words such as
reptile and *amphibian,* or *egg* and *bone.* Children can begin by saying *an* or
a as you name nouns. Later, they can say the whole phrase.

Picture It! Alike and Different

Read aloud the information and have children look at the pictures. Tell children
they can use information in writing and pictures to see how things are alike
and different. Discuss the items in the *Alike and Different* chart. Guide children
to add other items. (Alike: four legs; Different: shape of ears)

© Pearson Education, Inc. 2

Lesson 2: What are some ways mammals are adapted?

Vocabulary

*camouflage	environment	nonliving
adapt	living	

Activate Prior Knowledge/Build Background

Show children different colored images in front of different colored backgrounds. For example, place a white circle in front of white paper. Then, place a white circle in front of green paper. Discuss which image was harder to see and why. Explain that many animals have special colorations. This *camouflage* helps them sneak up on their prey or avoid predators.

Access Content

 Picture/Text Walk

Page 42: **Deer in summer and winter**
What animal is this? Explain that the mule deer is a mammal.
What does the deer look like in summer? What does it look like in winter? Do you think this change is a good thing? Why?
Help children see that the color of the deer's fur helps it blend into its environment. This is a special adaptation.

Pages 42–43: **Flying squirrel and chipmunk**
Explain that animals have certain body parts or can act in ways that help them live in their environment. The flying squirrel has special flaps of skin that allow it to glide long distances. The chipmunk lives in cold climates. Because there is not much food during the winter, it hoards food in the summer. Then, the chipmunk sleeps for most of the winter. Chipmunks eat some of the stored food every time they wake up.

Lesson 3: What are some ways birds are adapted?

Vocabulary

wings	penguin
feathers	waterproof

Activate Prior Knowledge/Build Background

Show a picture of a bird. **This is a bird. What is special about a bird?** Explain that a bird's wings and feathers help it fly. Discuss children's experiences with and knowledge about birds. Invite children to pantomime the act of flying.

Access Content

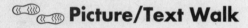 **Picture/Text Walk**

Page 44: **Nightjar and hummingbird**
These are birds. This is a nightjar. It has camouflage. The nightjar has feathers that help it hide from hungry animals. Explain that this is a kind of adaptation. It allows the nightjar to survive in its environment. **This is a hummingbird. It has a long beak that helps it get food.**

Page 45: **Penguin**
This bird is a penguin. It does not fly. It swims. It lives in cold water. Show how the penguin's wings are webbed. Explain that it also has waterproof feathers. They help keep the penguin dry and warm.

Extend Language

Have children work with the words *alike* and *different*. Explain that *alike* means similar. It does not have to mean identical. Compare different pictures in the chapter. Ask children to say *alike* or *different*.

Lesson 4: What are some ways fish are adapted?

Vocabulary

*gills	feelers
oxygen	whiskers

Activate Prior Knowledge/Build Background

Show a picture of a fish. **What animal is this? What is special about a fish?** Explain that fish live in water. They are adapted to that environment. They have gills so they can breathe in the water. They have fins so they can swim. Discuss children's experiences with and knowledge about fish.

Access Content

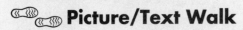 Picture/Text Walk

Pages 46–47: **Porcupine fish**
Show the normal and inflated pictures of the fish. **How is the fish different now?** Explain that this fish blows itself up when it gets scared. **How does this help this fish?** Explain that its spikes and ability to inflate are adaptations that protect the fish.

Extend Language

Explain that many fish get their names from animals that they look like or from special parts of their bodies. The porcupine fish gets its name from a porcupine, an animal covered in spikes. The feelers on a catfish's face look like the whiskers on a cat. The stingray has a stinger on its tail. Show other fish, such as a swordfish, a goldfish, or a hammerhead shark. Ask children where these fish might get their names.

Lesson 5: What are some ways reptiles are adapted?

Vocabulary

temperature

Activate Prior Knowledge/Build Background

 Picture/Text Walk

Page 48: **Snake**
What animal is this? What does it do? This is a snake. It is a reptile. Many reptiles have different adaptations. This snake's mouth is adapted to open very wide. It can swallow its food whole. Discuss children's knowledge about and experiences with snakes. Explain that snakes move without arms or legs. Snakes have scales. Not all snakes are venomous or aggressive.

Access Content

 Picture/Text Walk

Pages 48–49: **Chameleon**
This is a chameleon. A chameleon is a reptile. It has a long tongue. Explain that the tongue shoots out very quickly. It has a ball at the end of it. Prey sticks to this ball. **This tongue is an adaptation. It helps the chameleon catch food.**

Page 49: **Desert iguana**
This is a desert iguana. It is a reptile, too. Explain how reptiles cannot control their own body temperatures. If it is hot outside, their bodies are hot. If it is cold, their bodies are cold. **This iguana lives in the desert where it is hot. It has light skin to help it stay cool.**

Extend Language

Discuss the words *warm*, *hot*, *cold*, and *cool*. Have children repeat them. Ask children to describe today's temperature using one of these words. Discuss how today's temperature compares to yesterday's temperature.

Every Student Learns

Lesson 6: What are some ways amphibians are adapted?

Vocabulary

| amphibian | frog | toad |

Activate Prior Knowledge/Build Background

Hold up a picture of a frog. **What is this?** Remind children that frogs are amphibians. They live in the water when they are young. They move to land when they are grown. **Have you ever held a frog? What did it feel like?** Describe how frogs have smooth, wet skin; it helps them live in moist environments.

Access Content

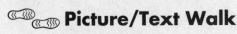 **Picture/Text Walk**

Page 50: **Tree frogs**
These are tree frogs. Tree frogs are amphibians. Many amphibians begin their lives in the water. When they are grown, they move to the land. Explain that tree frogs have very good eyesight. This adaptation allows them to find food in the dark.

Page 51: **Toad**
This is a toad. It is also an amphibian. Explain how toads dig into the ground when it is hot and dry. They look for food at night or when it rains.

Extend Language

Point to the tree frogs on page 50. Practice the location words: *left, middle, right*. Have children identify and repeat each location word after you say, for example, **This frog is on the left.** Later, give detailed commands or questions, such as **Point to the frog in the middle. Is this frog on the left or the right?**

© Pearson Education, Inc. 2

Lesson 7: What are some animals without backbones?

Vocabulary

*insects	abdomen
thorax	antennae

Activate Prior Knowledge/Build Background

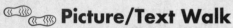 **Picture/Text Walk**

Pages 52–53: **Diving beetle**
**This is a beetle. It is an insect. How many legs does it have?
What other insects do you know?** Explain that insects do not have
bones. They have six legs and three body parts. Point to and name each
body part.

Access Content

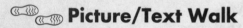 **Picture/Text Walk**

Page 52: **Walking stick**
**Is this an insect? What does it look like? Why does it look like a
stick?** Encourage children to recall the meaning of camouflage from Lesson 2.

Page 53: **Honeypot ants**
**These are honeypot ants. They store water and food in their
large abdomens.** Discuss how such an adaptation is helpful for
survival. Point out that honeypot ants share their water and food with
other ants.

Pages 54–55: **Octopus**
This is an octopus. Where does it live? Explain that an octopus does
not have bones. Point to the suction cups on its arms. Explain that the
cups help the octopus hold its food.

Extend Language

On the board, write the words *honeypot*, *backbone*, and *eyesight*. Read each
word aloud to the class. **How are all these words alike?** Elicit that in
each word, two smaller words are joined together to make a bigger word.
Call on a volunteer to draw a line between the two words that make up
each larger word. Discuss the meaning of each smaller word, and then the
meaning of the larger word. Point out that children can use the meanings
of the smaller words to try to figure out the meaning of the larger word.
You may wish to repeat this procedure with other compound words, such
as *newspaper*, *pigpen*, *sandbox*, *ladybug*, *eyebrow*, and *bedtime*.

Every Student Learns

Cause and Effect

Look at the pictures. Read the sentences. Tell a classmate what happens and why it happens.

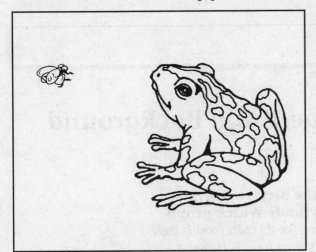

Cause: The frog is hungry.   Effect: The frog eats a fly.

Look at the picture below. Read the first sentence. Then finish the sentence that tells what happens. Draw a picture that shows what happens. Share your picture and sentence with a classmate.

Cause: The squirrel needs a place to live.   Effect: The squirrel _____

Lesson 1: What do plants and animals need?

Vocabulary

*producer	*consumer

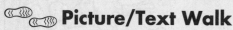

Activate Prior Knowledge/Build Background

Picture/Text Walk

Pages 70-71: **Producers and consumers**
What plants and animals do you see in the pictures? Which group of living things can make its own food? Which group cannot? Explain that a living thing that can make its own food is called a producer. A living thing that cannot make its own food is called a consumer. Invite children to name some of the producers and consumers in the picture. **Where do the consumers in this picture get their food?**

Pages 72-73: **Animals living together**
Explain that many plants and animals live together in a habitat. Point to the top picture on page 73. **Which animal needs more water? Which animal needs a larger shelter? Which can live in a smaller space?** Ask children if they can guess why a giraffe and a zebra can live in the same habitat without affecting each other's food supply. Explain that sometimes the number of animals in a habitat grows. **What happens when there is not enough food for all the animals in a habitat?**

Access Content

Invite children to list different animals they have seen living in the same habitat. The textbook shows water buffalo, zebra, and gazelles sharing the same water resource on a grassy plain. Children might think of squirrels, foxes, bears, and rabbits that live in a forest, or crabs, turtles, and birds that live near the sea. Discuss the different habitats of these animals, asking children to decide if the habitats are hot, cold, dry, wet, or someplace in the middle. Ask children to tell how each habitat helps the animals to meet their needs for food, water, and shelter.

Have teams of students make drawings showing some of the animals in the same habitat. Ask them to explain how the animals live together in the habitat.

Picture It! Cause and Effect

Explain that *cause* means why something happens. An *effect* is the result of the cause. Help children think of examples, such as the frog and squirrel pictures and help children identify the effect of each scene. (The frog eats a fly; the squirrel makes a nest.)

Every Student Learns

Lesson 2: How do plants and animals get food in a grassland?

Vocabulary

energy	*predator	*food web
*food chain	*prey	

Activate Prior Knowledge/Build Background

Ask for five volunteers. Give each child a large card. One card reads **Sun**, another **corn, vole, coyote,** and **lion.** Ask children to line up according to their order in the food chain. Ask other volunteers to help if necessary.

Invite the children to explain their order. For example, a student may say: **I am corn. I get what I need to make food from the Sun. But then a vole may eat me for energy.** Invite another group to do another food chain.

Access Content

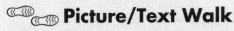 **Picture/Text Walk**

Pages 74–75: **A food chain**
What does the corn plant need to make food? What does the vole eat? How does the coyote get energy? Point out that some animals eat plants. Other animals eat those animals. Explain that in the food chain, an animal that eats another animal is called a predator. The animal it eats is called its prey. **Is the vole a predator or prey? What is the mountain lion?**

Pages 76–77: **A grassland food web**
What two animals eat the corn? What four animals eat the vole? Is there one food chain or many food chains in this habitat? Explain that when there are many food chains in a habitat, it is called a food web. **What are two food chains that go to the hawk? What other food chains do you see?**

Extend Language

Review the words *predator* and *prey*. Ask children how the two words are similar (they both begin with *pre-*, they are both nouns) and how they differ (*predator* is a bigger word with more letters). Point to the pictures of different animals on pages 76 and 77. Ask students to say whether the animal is a predator, prey, or both, and explain why. Suggest that one way to avoid confusing these two words is to remember that in real life, the predator (the bigger word) is often bigger than its prey (the smaller word).

Lesson 3: How do plants and animals get food in an ocean?

Activate Prior Knowledge/Build Background

Ask children if they have seen an ocean or a picture of an ocean on television or in books. Invite them to describe the kinds of animals and plants that are found in and around the ocean in rock pools. (seaweed, mussels, crabs, shrimp, fish, sharks, coral, whales, etc.) Discuss what the basic needs of these living things might be. (food, space, etc.)

Access Content

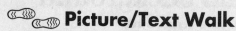 **Picture/Text Walk**

Pages 78–79: **An ocean food chain**
Explain that these pictures show a food chain in the ocean. The food chain begins with kelp. Kelp are plants that grow in the ocean. They use sunlight to make food. **Does energy go from kelp to the sea otter or from the sea otter to kelp? How does energy go from the Sun to the sea otter?** Discuss each link in the chain. Ask children why this is called a food chain. Encourage comparisons by sketching a simple linked chain on the board.

Pages 80–81: **An ocean food web**
Identify the picture as an ocean food web. **How many food chains can you count? What animal eats the sea urchin?** The kelp uses energy from the Sun to make food. **Then what happens? Where does the energy from the sea star end up?** Ask children why this is called a food web. Encourage comparisons by sketching the web on the board and filling it in with the children.

Extend Language

Point out that a group of seagulls is called a flock. Explain that we use *flock* to talk about a group of birds. Ask students what they think a school of fish is. Explain that the word *school* can also mean a group of water animals that swim together. Have students write and illustrate sentences with the words *flock* and *school*.

Lesson 4: What can cause a food web to change?

Vocabulary

ship	oil
accident	spilled

Activate Prior Knowledge/Build Background

Have children brainstorm a list of things that can get clothes dirty. Show children a product that is used to remove stains and ask if they have something similar at home. Invite children to name some things that stain and are hard to clean off (oil, ketchup, paint). Read the label on the stain remover and tell children what kinds of stains it removes.

Access Content

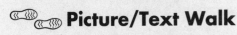 **Picture/Text Walk**

Pages 82–83: **An oil spill**
Explain that the ship in the picture on page 82 had an accident. Oil spilled from the ship. **Where did the oil go?** Point to the three otters. **How did these otters get covered in oil? What else could have been covered in oil?** (other ocean animals, plants like seaweed) Point to the clean otter. **How do you think this otter got clean?** When the oil spilled from this ship, people helped clean the water and the animals. **What do you think happened to the animals and plants that people did not clean?** Explain that sometimes people cause a change in a food web. A change can hurt parts of a food web.

Extend Language

Remind children that a *producer* is a living thing that can make its own food. A *consumer* is a living thing that cannot make its own food. Invite children to draw a picture that shows both a producer and a consumer in an ocean food web and how they could be affected by an oil spill.

Lesson 5: How do plants and animals help each other?

Vocabulary

ant	nest
protect	feathers

Activate Prior Knowledge/Build Background

Invite children to talk about a time when they helped someone. Have them describe what the other person needed and how they helped. Then ask students to talk about a time when someone helped them. Finally, ask children to describe a relationship in which they help someone and that person helps them too. Explain that plants and animals can also help each other.

Access Content

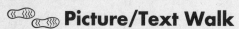 **Picture/Text Walk**

Pages 84–85: Animal and plant protection
Point to the picture on page 85, on the right. **This is a sea urchin. It has long sharp spines. Can you find another animal in the picture? Is the cardinal fish safe from bigger fish when it stays close to the sea urchin? Why?** Point to the picture on page 84. **These ants live inside this plant. The ants can bite. How do you think the ants protect the plant? How does the plant help the ants?**

Pages 86–87: Different nests
Explain that some animals use parts of plants and animals to build their nests. Point to the squirrel's nest on page 87. **What did the squirrel use to make its nest? Can you find the bird feathers?** Ask children to look at page 86. **What does the owl use to make its nest? What do you think the masked weaver bird will do with the plant parts it finds?**

Pages 88–89: Animals need each other
Point to the picture of the remora fish and the shark. **The little fish needs protection and food. How does the shark help the fish?** Point to the rhinoceros and the egret. **This bird eats flies and insects. How do you think the rhinoceros helps the bird get its food? How does the bird help the rhinoceros?**

Extend Language

Write the words *sea* and *see*. Note that the two words are pronounced the same, but have different meanings. Review the two words and encourage children to make up sentences that use both words.

© Pearson Education, Inc. 2

🎯 Infer

Look at the picture. Read the sentences. Then use what you know to answer the question.

This is a sea turtle.
It just hatched from
an egg.

Is this a baby sea turtle or an adult sea turtle?

**Now look at this picture. Read the sentences.
Then use what you know to answer the question.**

This is a saguaro cactus.
A saguaro cactus grows
arms when it is about 65
years old.

Is this cactus 20 years old or 80 years old?

Lesson 1: How do sea turtles grow and change?

Vocabulary

lay	tooth
hatch	*life cycle

Activate Prior Knowledge/Build Background

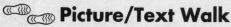 **Picture/Text Walk**

Pages 102–103: **Sea turtles**
What is the living turtle doing? Is the toy turtle a living thing?
Explain that plants and animals are living things. **Does the toy turtle need food? Can it grow? What can the living turtle do that the toy turtle cannot do?**

Pages 104–105: **Sea turtle eggs**
Where does this turtle live? Where does it lay its eggs? Explain that after two months, baby turtles come out of an egg, or *hatch*. **Baby turtles have a special tooth. How does this baby turtle use its tooth to hatch?**

Pages 106–107 **A sea turtle's life cycle**
Explain that a life cycle is how a living thing grows and changes. **What are the three parts of the sea turtle's life cycle? How does a new life cycle start?** Ask children why the arrows that show the life cycle go around in a circle instead of in a straight line.

Access Content

Bring in a boiled chicken egg. Ask children to name the animal that lays this kind of egg. Together, brainstorm a list of animals that lay eggs. Then ask children to describe the life cycle of a chicken or another animal they know.

Extend Language

Point to the picture of the turtle's life cycle on pages 106–107. Discuss how the arrows in a circle show that the life cycle goes around, repeating with each new egg. Ask children if they know any other words that include the word *cycle.* (bicycle, tricycle, recycle) Discuss the meanings of the words.

Picture It! Infer

Explain that *infer* means to use what you know to answer a question. Discuss the pictures and text. What clues show that the turtle is a baby and that the cactus must be 80 years old?

Every Student Learns

Lesson 2: What is the life cycle of a dragonfly?

Vocabulary

| insects | *nymphs | wings |

Activate Prior Knowledge/Build Background

Provide children with pictures of different insects in different stages of their life cycles. Ask children to tell what they know about insects. Talk about insects that fly and insects that don't fly. Discuss whether children think insects that fly are able to fly when they hatch from their eggs.

Access Content

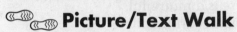 **Picture/Text Walk**

Pages 108–109: **The life cycle of a dragonfly**
Point to the picture of the adult dragonfly. **What kind of animal is this? What is the name of this insect? How does it move around? Do dragonflies lay eggs?** Explain that young insects are called nymphs. **Where does a dragonfly nymph live when it hatches? Does it have wings?** Explain that first the nymph lives in the water, and then it lives on the land. **How does the nymph change when it grows into a dragonfly? What happens next in the life cycle of a dragonfly?**

Extend Language

Write the word *nymph*. Pronounce the word slowly and then have children pronounce the word together. Ask them what sound the letters *p* and *h* make in *nymph*. Explain that when *p* and *h* are together in a word, they are pronounced like the letter *f*. Write the following words: *telephone*, *photo*, *graph*. Have a student circle the *ph* combinations in the three words. Then help them pronounce each word.

Lesson 3: What is the life cycle of a horse?

Vocabulary

young	foal
mammal	adult

Activate Prior Knowledge/Build Background

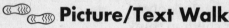 **Picture/Text Walk**

Pages 110–111: **The life cycle of a horse**
Point to the adult horse on the right. **What is this animal called?**
Explain that a young horse is called a foal. **Do foals grow in eggs like sea turtles and dragonflies?** Explain that a horse is a mammal. Young mammals grow inside their mothers. Young mammals drink milk from their mother. **Does the foal look like the adult horse? How is it the same? How is it different? Is the foal old enough to have more foals? Is the adult horse old enough to have foals?**

Access Content

Remind children that mammals grow inside their mothers, not inside eggs. Young mammals drink milk from their mothers. Invite children to brainstorm a list of animals that are mammals. Ask children to check that every animal on the list has both characteristics of mammals. Then discuss with children how all or some of these animals are alike and how they are different.

Every Student Learns

Lesson 4: How are young animals like their parents?

Vocabulary

parents	kittens
penguins	giraffes

Activate Prior Knowledge/Build Background

Invite children who have or once had animals to tell what the animals were like when they were young and when they were older. Ask them to tell how the young animals and their parents were alike and how they were different.

Access Content

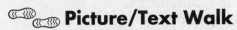 **Picture/Text Walk**

Pages 112–113: **Young animals and their parents**
Point to the penguins. **This is a young penguin and one of its parents. How are they alike? How are they different?** Explain that when the young penguin grows, its feathers turn white and black like the feathers of its parents. **These kittens all have the same parents. How are they all alike? How is each one different from the other kittens? How are the giraffes alike and different? Do you think the spots on the young giraffe are the same as the spots on the adult giraffe?** Explain that the spots on a young giraffe get darker when it grows up.

Extend Language

Remind children that a young cat is called a kitten. Explain that many animals have two names: one for the young animal and one for the adult animal. Write the following pairs of animal names: cat/kitten, dog/pup (or puppy), chicken/chick, duck/duckling, pig/piglet. Help children make up a sentence that uses the name for each adult animal and another sentence with the name of each young animal.

Lesson 5: What is the life cycle of a bean plant?

Vocabulary

seed	roots	leaves
*seed coat	*seedling	flowers
*germinate	stem	

Activate Prior Knowledge/Build Background

Divide children into small groups and give each child an unshelled peanut. If the peanuts have been cooked or roasted, explain to children that they are cooked seeds that cannot grow. Invite children to closely observe their peanuts. First, ask children to open the shell. Then ask them to take the thin, brown covering off the peanut. Finally, ask them to carefully open each peanut in halves. Ask them to record their observations as a group and then tell the class what they have found.

Access Content

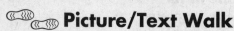 **Picture/Text Walk**

Pages 114–115: **A bean plant grows**
Point to the picture of the bean seed on the far left. **What happens to the bean seed?** Explain that every seed has a very small plant and food for it inside. Point to the second picture to the left. **A seed can germinate when it has enough water and air.** *Germinate* **means to start to grow. What part of this plant is opening the seed coat of the bean?** Point to the seedling. **A young plant is called a** *seedling.* Help children identify the roots, stem, and leaves of the seedling. **Where do the roots grow? Where does the stem grow?** Point to the adult plant. **How is the adult bean plant different from the seedling?** Explain that an adult bean plant grows flowers. **What do flowers make that can grow into new plants?**

© Pearson Education, Inc. **2**

Lesson 6: How are young plants like their parents?

Vocabulary

color	shape

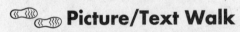

Activate Prior Knowledge/Build Background

Make a list with children of different kinds of plants they know. Discuss what each plant looks like when it is young. Then talk about what each plant looks like when it is an adult. Compare the young plants to the adult plants and say how they are alike and how they are different.

Access Content

Picture/Text Walk

Pages 116–117: **Saguaro cactuses and foxgloves**
Point to the two saguaro cactuses. Explain that a saguaro cactus can live for more than 100 years. **Which cactus is the young saguaro cactus? Which is the adult saguaro cactus. How are they alike? How are they different?** Explain that a young saguaro cactus grows straight up from the ground. It begins to grow arms when it is about 65 years old. Point to the foxgloves. **How are the foxglove flowers alike? How are they different?**

Extend Language

Point out that the name of a plant sometimes give clues about what a part of that plant looks like. Write *foxglove, blueberry, evergreen, lady slipper,* and *prickly pear* on the board. Show children pictures of each plant and discuss how each name tells us something about that plant.

Lesson 7: How do people grow and change?

Vocabulary

baby	children	exactly
child	teenager	

Activate Prior Knowledge/Build Background

Invite children to work in pairs for role play. Ask each pair to choose a different animal. Ask each pair to discuss what the young animal is like and how it differs from the adult animal. Then ask one student in each pair to role play the young animal and the other to role play the adult. After children have had a chance to practice, finish by having each pair present their animal role play for the class.

Access Content

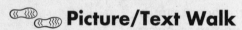 **Picture/Text Walk**

Page 118: **A growing boy**
All people change as they grow. **Is this boy a baby or a child? What are some ways a child is different from a baby?** You used to be a baby. Now you are a child. **What are some ways you have changed?**

Page 119: **A growing family**
Do you think these boys will grow taller? Explain that a child grows and becomes a teenager. A teenager grows and becomes an adult. Adults grow too. **Does an adult grow taller? Can their hair change when they grow? What are other ways adults can change?**

Page 120: **Children are alike and different**
How are these children alike? How are they different? Point out that some people are short and some people are tall. **What are other ways people are different?** Point to the two pairs of brothers. **How are the brothers alike? How are they different?**

Page 121: **People in the same family**
Children can look like their parents. **How are these children like their parents? How are they different from their parents? Do people in the same family look exactly alike?**

Every Student Learns

Picture Clues

Look at the picture. Read the paragraph. As you read each sentence, point to the picture clue that matches what you read.

Water in the Summer

We use a lot of water in the summer. My father waters the flowers in the garden. We drink a lot of water when it is hot. We also like to play in the water.

Draw a picture that shows people using three things made from trees. Tell a classmate about your picture. Be sure to point out your picture clues.

Lesson 1: What are natural resources?

Vocabulary

*natural resource	oil	coal

Activate Prior Knowledge/Build Background

 Picture/Text Walk

Pages 142–143: **Earth's natural resources**
Explain that resources are things people can use. Natural resources are things people can use that come from Earth. **What natural resources do you see in this picture?** Point to the tree. **How do people use trees?** Point out that when people use trees they can plant new trees. Explain that oil and coal are also natural resources. **When people use oil and coal, can they make more?** Explain that some natural resources—like sunlight, water, and air—can never be used up.

Pages 144–145: **Water and air**
What natural resource is inside the soccer ball and the balloon? Where can we find air? What natural resource is the person giving to the plant? Where can we find freshwater on Earth? Where can we find saltwater? What are some ways people use water?

Access Content

Brainstorm with students a list of the natural resources they use during a typical school day. Remind them to think of the things they eat and drink, what their clothing is made of, and the resources that are used in their home and at school. You might want to lead students through the 24 hours of their day, starting from the time they wake up.

Picture It! Picture Clues

Ask children to read the sentences as they point to the part of the picture that matches each sentence. Then guide children as they draw and describe a picture that shows people making or using wood products.

Lesson 2: What are rocks and soil like?

Vocabulary

*boulder	*minerals	soil
*sand	humus	

Activate Prior Knowledge/Build Background

Divide the class into small groups. Distribute a clear, sealed plastic bag partly filled with small rocks, sand, and different kinds of soil to each group. Provide the groups with magnifying glasses and invite children to carefully examine the contents of their bag. Ask children to record their observations. Invite each group to share their observations with the class.

Access Content

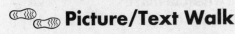 **Picture/Text Walk**

Pages 146–147: **Kinds of rocks**
What kinds of rocks do you see in this picture? Explain that a very large rock is called a boulder. Sand is made of very small pieces of rock. **What do you think breaks these rocks into sand?**

Page 147: **Kinds of minerals**
Explain that rocks are minerals. Minerals are nonliving things that come from Earth. **What do you think quartz is used for?** Explain that lapis is another mineral. **What are the names of some other minerals?** (iron, gold, silver)

Pages 148–149: **Kinds of soil**
These are different kinds of soil. Humus is a part of soil that comes from living things. Clay soil feels soft and sticky. What is sandy soil like? Explain that different kinds of plants grow best in different kinds of soil.

Extend Language

Point out that the word *rock* can be used as a verb as well as a noun. Explain that the verb *rock* means "to move back and forth or from side to side." Help students to make sentences that use *rock* as a noun and as a verb.

Lesson 3: How do people use plants?

Vocabulary

cotton   wheat

Activate Prior Knowledge/Build Background

Picture/Text Walk

Pages 150–151: **Ways people use plants**
Explain to children that plants are a natural resource, like rocks and soil.
People use wood from trees. **What is something in these pictures
that people make from wood? What other thing in these
pictures do people make from trees? What are some ways people
use paper?** Explain to children that people use cotton to make clothes.
What do you see that is made of cotton? People use wheat to make
food. **What is one kind of food people make from wheat?**

Access Content

Remind students that paper and wood both come from trees. Make a
list with students of everything in the classroom that is made from trees.
Remind them to look at small things such as pencils and the heels of their
shoes, as well as big things such as furniture and parts of the classroom
itself. Then brainstorm a second list of things made of wood or paper that
students have seen outside the classroom.

Extend Language

Point out that the word *plant* can also be used as a verb and as a noun.
Explain that the verb *plant* means "to put in the ground or soil to grow."
Help students to make sentences that use *plant* as a noun and as a verb.

Lesson 4: How does Earth change?

Vocabulary

*erosion   *weathering

Activate Prior Knowledge/Build Background

Show students a pot of loose, dry soil and a pot of moist soil with a plant firmly rooted in it. Help students gently shake each pot enough to see which soil moves around and which soil doesn't. Ask students to talk about how plants keep soil from moving. Ask them to say what they think would happen to the soil in each pot if a strong wind blew on them or a lot of rain fell on them suddenly.

Access Content

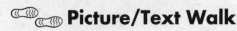 Picture/Text Walk

Page 152: **Erosion**
Explain that water and wind can move rocks and soil. Point to the erosion in the picture. **What do you think made this erosion happen? Why is most of the erosion in the place where there are no plants? How do plants help stop erosion from happening?**

Page 153: **Weathering**
Explain that weathering is when rocks change and when they break apart. Point to the picture of the cracked earth. **What do you think made this weathering happen?** Explain that water and changes in temperature can cause weathering. Point to the gopher. **How can animals change Earth?**

Extend Language

Point out that children can remember that *weathering* is a result of water and changes in temperature by looking at the base word: *weather*. Invite children to make as many small words as they can from the letters in the word *weathering*.

Lesson 5: How can people help protect Earth?

Vocabulary

*pollution	*recycle
reduce	reuse

Activate Prior Knowledge/Build Background

Discuss with children what it means to reuse something. Show them an empty can. Invite small groups of students to brainstorm ways they could reuse the can. Ask each group to make a poster that shows three ways to reuse a can.

Access Content

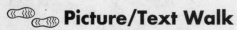 **Picture/Text Walk**

Pages 154–155: **Pollution**
Point to the landscape. **What are some things people do that hurt Earth?** Explain that pollution happens when something is added to the land, air, or water that can hurt plants or animals. Explain that people today are trying to make less pollution and that smoke stacks like those on page 154 make less air pollution.

Pages 156–157: **Reduce, reuse, recycle**
How did people use the plastic from these milk cartons again? Explain that to *recycle* means to change something so it can be used again. Explain that people can recycle glass, paper, plastic, and metal. People also take care of Earth when they reuse things. Remind children that *reuse* means to use again. People can also reduce what they use. *Reduce* means to use less of something.

Page 158: **Plants and animals**
Explain that forests are always changing. **How can this campfire start a forest fire? What happens to trees and animals when there is a forest fire?** Point out that people also cut down trees to get the wood. **People plant new trees. New trees take a long time to grow into big, tall trees.**

Page 159: **Protecting plants and animals**
Explain that the bird on page 159 lives in a refuge. A refuge is a safe place for plants and animals to live. People cannot build on a refuge. **What can happen on land outside a refuge? Why do some plants and animals need to live in a refuge?**

Every Student Learns

Name _____

⊙Draw Conclusions

Look at the picture. Read the sentences. Then write the name of the season on the line under the sentences.

It is cool outside now. Birds migrate every day. The leaves on the trees are red, yellow, and orange. Some brown leaves are on the ground. Winter is coming.

_____

Draw conclusions. Look at the picture. Then fill in two statements about the season.

It is a warm day. The rain falls all day. The trees have new green leaves. A mother deer stands under a tree with her babies.

_____ is over.

_____ is here.

Lesson 1: What are some kinds of weather?

Vocabulary

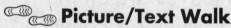

temperature	snow	drought
wind	clouds	
sleet	freeze	

Activate Prior Knowledge/Build Background

Picture/Text Walk

Page 175: **Windy weather**
How do you know what to wear when you wake up? Explain that weather is what the air is like outside. **What does temperature tell you about the air?** Point to the kite. **What kind of weather do you need to fly a kite? What moves when there is wind?**

Pages 176–177: **Wet and dry weather**
What kinds of weather do you see in these pictures? When does it snow? When does it rain? Explain that rain, sleet, and snow are three kinds of wet weather. Clouds are made of very small drops of water. **What do you call drops of water that fall from clouds? What do you call rain that freezes when it falls? What falls from clouds when the air is very cold?** Point to the picture of the drought. **Is this wet or dry weather?** Explain that a drought can happen when there is no rain for a long time.

Access Content

Invite children to tell about their experiences in different kinds of wet and dry weather. Make a two-column chart with the title *Weather*. Record children's comments under the subheadings *Kind of Weather* and *What It Is Like*.

Picture It! Draw Conclusions

Discuss the picture and sentences about fall. Ask questions that will encourage children to draw conclusions. Does the weather change in fall? How do you know? What do birds do in the fall? Do you think they migrate in other seasons? Why not? Repeat with the spring picture and text.

Every Student Learns

Lesson 2: What is the water cycle?

Vocabulary

*water cycle	*evaporate
*condense	*water vapor

Activate Prior Knowledge/Build Background

Ask children to talk about times they saw something dry out. It might have been an item of clothing, something wet that spilled, something dry that was exposed to the air for a long time, or a body of water such as a puddle or stream. Discuss with children what makes things dry out faster or slower and where the water goes when things get dry.

Access Content

✑✑ Picture/Text Walk

Pages 178–179: **The water cycle**
Explain that water moves from the clouds to Earth and back to the clouds again. This is called the water cycle. **What arrow in this picture shows where water falls from the clouds? Where does the water go on Earth? What happens next to the water?** Explain that energy from the Sun makes water evaporate. Water changes into water vapor. **Is water vapor water on Earth or water in the air?** Point to the top box. Explain that when water vapor in the air gets cold, it condenses. *Condense* means to change into very small drops of water. **What are clouds made of? What happens when the water cycle starts again?**

Extend Language

Review the words *evaporate* and *condense*. To help children practice these words, write each one on an index card. Draw a diagram with arrows that show water rising into the air and then condensing into a cloud of tiny drops. Have children take turns matching the index cards to the two parts of the diagram.

Lesson 3: What is spring?

Vocabulary

seasons	rainy

Activate Prior Knowledge/Build Background

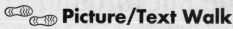 **Picture/Text Walk**

Pages 180–181: **Things that happen in the spring**
What are the four seasons? What season is it in these pictures?
What are some things that happen in the spring? What can the
weather be like in the spring? Point out that the days in spring are
longer than the days in winter. **What are other ways that spring is**
different from winter? Point out to children that many animals have
babies in the spring.

Access Content

Have small groups of children create short scenes that show what spring
is like. Ask them to first discuss what they know happens in spring. Then
have them practice acting these events out with gestures and pantomime.
Have each group present their spring scene to the class. Ask the children
who are watching to say what the children in each scene are showing.

Extend Language

Remind children of the names of the seasons: spring, summer, fall, and
winter. To help children practice the order of the seasons, write the name
of each on a separate index card. Shuffle the cards, and then have small
groups of children take turns putting the cards in their correct order and
then reading them aloud.

© Pearson Education, Inc. **2**

Every Student Learns

Lesson 4: What is summer?

Vocabulary

daylight	vegetables

Activate Prior Knowledge/Build Background

Ask children to mention different things that happen during the summer.
Remind them to include activities, special events or holidays, and foods
they eat in the summer. Make a list with the title *What Happens in the
Summer?* Put a check mark next to the things that happen that children
like and an *X* next to things they don't like.

Access Content

Picture/Text Walk

Pages 182–183: **Things that happen in the summer**
Explain that these summer pictures are from South Carolina. **What is
summer like in South Carolina? What is the weather like in the
day? What is the weather like at night?** Point to the picture of the
park. **What is this place? What plants grow in a park? What
do people do in a park in the summer?** Point to the garden. **What
grows in a garden in the summer?** Point to the picture of the bears
and the ducks. **What are these animal families doing? What are
some things animal babies do in the summer?**

Extend Language

Ask children which two words make up the word *daylight*. Explain that
this type of word is called a compound noun. Ask children to think of
other words that are compound nouns (cookout, butterfly, bookend).
Invite them to write and illustrate the words on a poster.

Lesson 5: What is fall?

Vocabulary

shorter	store
cooler	*migrate

Activate Prior Knowledge/Build Background

Discuss with children what different plants do in the fall. Talk about the kinds of crops that farmers might harvest in different seasons. Ask children which foods they think might be eaten especially in the fall and where those foods come from. Make a list of fall foods with the title *Food We Like to Eat in the Fall.*

Access Content

Pages 184–185: **Things that happen in the fall**
Explain to children that these are pictures from Indiana. **What is fall like in Indiana?** Explain that the days are shorter in the fall than in the summer. **Does the temperature of the air get warmer or cooler in the fall? What happens to the leaves on some trees?** Point to the squirrel on page 184. **What is this animal doing?** Explain that in the fall some animals store food so they have something to eat in the winter. Point to the flying cranes. **Where are these birds going?** Explain that some animals migrate in the fall. *Migrate* means to move to a warmer place. **Why do you think animals migrate in the fall?** Point to the bottom picture on page 185. **What do farmers do in the fall? When did these plants grow?**

Extend Language

Point out that the word *warmer* comes from the adjective *warm*. The *-er* ending means "more." We add *-er* to adjectives when we compare two different things; for example, "the garden is warmer than the park." Have children make sentences about the seasons using the comparative adjectives *warmer, cooler, shorter,* and *longer.*

Lesson 6: What is winter?

Vocabulary

> *hibernate

Activate Prior Knowledge/Build Background

Invite children to tell about their different experiences of winter.
Encourage them to talk about what the weather was like, what kinds of
clothes they wore, and what they did in the winter. Make lists of adjectives
that describe winter in different places.

Access Content

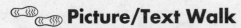 Picture/Text Walk

Pages 186–187: **Things that happen in the winter**
Explain to children that these are pictures from the state of New York.
**What do you see on the trees and the house? What is the
weather like in the winter here? What can happen to the water
in ponds and streams? What are some things that people do
in the winter?** Explain that some animals hibernate in the winter.
Hibernate means to have a deep sleep for a long time. Point to the picture
on page 186. **What is the bear doing? Where is it hibernating?**
Explain that animals that hibernate wake up in the spring. Then they
look for food.

Extend Language

Help children practice pronunciation strategies by breaking the word *hibernate*
into syllables. Invite children to clap the number of syllables as you say
the word slowly. Ask children to identify the vowels in each syllable.
Discuss the sound that each vowel makes in this particular word.

Lesson 7: What are some kinds of bad weather?

Vocabulary

thunderstorm	*tornado	basement
*lightning	funnel	*hurricane

Activate Prior Knowledge/Build Background

Ask children to tell about times when they experienced bad weather. Have them talk about what it was like, what happened, and how people stayed safe. Encourage children to use sounds and gestures to describe the weather.

Access Content

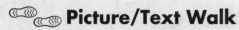 **Picture/Text Walk**

Pages 188–189: **A thunderstorm**
What is this flash of light called? Explain that a thunderstorm is when it rains a lot and there is thunder and lightning. **What does thunder sound like?** Tell children that when there is a thunderstorm, they should go into a building or car and stay away from water, metal, trees, and things that use electricity.

Pages 190–191: **A tornado**
Explain that a tornado is a very strong wind that comes down from the clouds. A tornado can happen in a thunderstorm. **What shape does a tornado have? What happens when a tornado touches something?** Tell children that when there is a tornado, they should go to a safe place such as the basement, a place inside that does not have windows, or under the stairs. If they cannot go inside, they should lie down in a low place. They should cover their heads.

Pages 192–193: **A hurricane**
Explain that a hurricane is a big storm that starts over the ocean where there is warm water. Point to the small picture. **What is a hurricane like? What can happen when a lot of rain falls on land?** Explain that a hurricane can knock over trees and buildings. Tell children that when there is a hurricane, people should stay indoors, far from the ocean. Discuss why people cover their windows with boards, keep extra water and batteries, and stay inside.

© Pearson Education, Inc. 2

Every Student Learns

Retell

Look at the picture. Read the paragraph. Then tell what you learned about the Triceratops.

Triceratops

The Triceratops was a dinosaur. It had three horns on its head. It had a very big head. The Triceratops ate plants. It walked on four legs and moved slowly.

Retell
Complete the sentences.

The Triceratops was a _____.

It had three_____ on its head.

It had a very big _____.

Retell three things about the Triceratops.

_____

_____

_____

Lesson 1: How can we learn about the past?

Vocabulary

*fossil   *paleontologist

Activate Prior Knowledge/Build Background

 **Picture/Text Walk**

Pages 206–207: **Learning about the past**
Use the pictures on pages 206–207 to elicit a discussion. **Does this picture show a scene from now or from a long time ago?** (page 206) **How do you know?** Then, point to the photo of the paleontologists on page 207. **These scientists study fossils. Fossils are remains of plants and animals that lived long ago. Scientists who study fossils are called paleontologists.** Discuss the kinds of activities the scientists are doing, such as marking the land with a grid, digging, and sifting sand looking for fossil rocks and bones. **What do you think these paleontologists are hoping to find?**

Pages 208–209: **How a fossil is formed**
Point out the lizard fossil on page 208. **This is a fossil of a lizard that lived long ago.** Use the sequence of pictures on 209 to explain how the lizard fossil was formed. **The lizard died in the pond and sank to the bottom. Then, sand and mud covered the lizard. What did the sand and mud turn into?** Point to the other fossils. **A fossil can be a print of an animal or plant, or of a footprint of an animal.**

Access Content

Invite children to tell about animal prints they have seen, including tracks made in the mud, in the snow, and dirty tracks made indoors. Ask them to talk about how these prints are like fossils and how they are different. Provide children with drawing paper and crayons. Have children trace the outline of one hand on the paper. Discuss how these tracings are like and different from fossils.

Picture It! Retell

Guide children to look at the picture of the Triceratops before trying to do the Retell exercises. Read the paragraph with them, and remind them that they can get help in doing the Retell charts by looking back at the picture and paragraph. Go over the answers with them (dinosaur, horns, head). Accept all possible answers for the sentences.

Lesson 2: What can we learn from fossils?

Vocabulary

*extinct   habitat

Activate Prior Knowledge/Build Background

Discuss with children what they learned about fossils. (Possible responses: They are of plants and animals that lived long ago, they are prints of plants, animals and footprints in rock, it takes many years for fossils to form.) **What do you think scientists can learn from studying fossils?**

Access Content

Picture/Text Walk

Pages 210–211: **Fossils of extinct plants and animals**
Point to the fossil on page 211. **This is a fossil of an Archaeopteryx.** Model the pronunciation for them. Explain that the Archaeopteryx is extinct. An extinct plant or animal no longer lives on Earth. Explain that sometimes a habitat cannot give the plants and animals that live there what they need. Then the plants and animals may disappear forever. **Fossils tell us the size and shape of plants and animals that lived long ago. What does the fossil tell us about the Archaeopteryx? What animal today does it look like?** Point to the fossil on page 210. **What does this fossil tell us about this extinct plant?**

Extend Language

Review the word *extinct*. Make a two-column chart with *Living Today* as the left column header and *Extinct* as the right column header. Write *Archaeopteryx* in the right column. Ask children to give you the names of animals that are living today and animals that are extinct. Encourage children to give the names of dinosaurs they know about from their reading and add them to the *Extinct* column.

Lesson 3: What were dinosaurs like?

Vocabulary

*dinosaur

Activate Prior Knowledge/Build Background

Provide children with illustrations of a human skeleton. Have them study the human skeleton in small groups. Ask them to study the skeleton the way a paleontologist studies a fossil. What can they learn about people from their bones? Have each group present its conclusions to the class.

Access Content

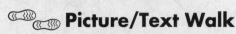 **Picture/Text Walk**

Pages 212–213: **Kinds of dinosaurs**
What are these animals called? (dinosaurs) **Are dinosaurs alive today or are they extinct?** Explain that dinosaurs lived long ago and are now extinct. Use the pictures and captions to point out that some dinosaurs were small, and others were very large. **About how large was a Compsognathus? About how large was a Barosaurus? What did dinosaurs eat?** (some ate plants, some ate animals)

Pages 214–215: **What dinosaur fossils tell us that Paleontologists can find out what dinosaurs looked like by studying fossils of their bones.** Point to the Triceratops. **How did a Triceratops protect itself?** Point to the Tyrannosaurus rex. **Look at the Tyrannosaurus rex's sharp teeth. What do you think it ate?** Point to the Stegosaurus skeleton on page 215. **The Stegosaurus had a big body. Why did it need a habitat with many plants?**

Extend Language

Point out to children that *bone* is used in some expressions. Write *bone dry* and *skin and bones*. Explain that *bone dry* is an expression that means "very dry" and that *skin and bones* means "very thin." Write *I saw a dog that was skin and bones*. Ask children to explain the meaning of this sentence. Then have them think of new sentences with each expression.

Lesson 4: What are some new discoveries?

Activate Prior Knowledge/Build Background

Ask children to tell what they know about birds and their eggs. Discuss where different birds keep their eggs. **Why do birds need to protect their eggs? What do birds do to protect their eggs?**

Access Content

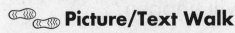 **Picture/Text Walk**

Pages 216–217: **Oviraptor eggs**
Point to the fossil eggs on page 216. **What do these fossils look like?** Explain that they are fossil eggs. **Paleontologists found fossils of a small dinosaur called an Oviraptor near some fossils of eggs. They thought the Oviraptor was stealing the eggs to eat them.** Point to page 217. **Later, paleontologists found a fossil of an Oviraptor sitting on the same kind of eggs. Now they think the Oviraptor was keeping its own eggs safe.**

Extend Language

Write the following sentences on the board: *The Oviraptor is a dinosaur. What kind of dinosaur is it?* Underline the word *kind*. Tell children that in this sentence *kind* means "sort or type." Then write the following sentence on the board: *The kind man smiled.* Point out that the word *kind* can have more than one meaning. In this sentence, it is not a noun but an adjective that means "nice." Ask children to write a sentence using the word *kind*. Call on a few volunteers to read their sentences aloud. Have children identify the meaning of *kind* in each sentence.

🎯 Draw Conclusions

Look at the picture. Read the question. Write what you know in the first box. Write your conclusion in the second box.

The ice cubes are in a warm room. What do you think will happen?

I Know		**Conclusion**
Warm air makes ice melt.	→	The ice cubes will melt.

Maritza blows air into the balloon. What do you think will happen?

I Know		**Conclusion**
Air is a gas. Gas fills its container.	→	

Every Student Learns

Lesson 1: What is matter?

Vocabulary

*mass	observe	weight
*property	senses	

Activate Prior Knowledge/Build Background

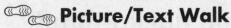 **Picture/Text Walk**

Page 239: **Matter**
Explain that everything around us is made of matter. Matter is anything that takes up space and has weight. **What is made of matter in this classroom?** Point out that some things we cannot see, such as air, are made of matter. **Everything made of matter has mass. Mass is how much matter there is in something.**

Pages 240–241: **Properties of matter**
Point to different objects pictured and ask children to describe them. **What color is it? What shape is it? What size is it?** Point out that different kinds of matter have different properties. Color, shape, and size are some properties. Explain that a property is something about an object that you can observe with your senses—by seeing, hearing, smelling, and feeling. **How do you think the pipe cleaners feel?**

Access Content

Pass around a collection of objects, including a chalkboard eraser, a pencil with an eraser, and a paperclip. Remind students that all of these objects are made of matter. We describe matter by saying what its properties are. Have students describe the properties of each object. Record their descriptions on a five-column chart with the following headings: *Color, Shape, Size, Weight, How It Feels.*

Picture It! Draw Conclusions

Explain that the first box tells what you know and the second box is for the conclusion. Have students read the first fact and conclusion. Then have students write a conclusion for the second picture. (Possible answers: *The air will fill the balloon; Maritza will fill the balloon with air.*)

Lesson 2: What are the states of matter?

Vocabulary

*states of matter	*liquid
*solid	*gas

Activate Prior Knowledge/Build Background

Display a glass of water and an un-inflated balloon. Point to the glass. Ask children to describe the properties of the glass. **Does the glass have a shape?** Then point to the water inside. **Does the water have a shape? What shape does it have?** Blow up the balloon a little and then a little more. Ask children what is filling the balloon. **Does breath, or air, have a shape?**

Access Content

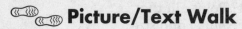 **Picture/Text Walk**

Pages 242–243: **States of matter, solids**
The three states of matter are solids, liquids, and gases. Explain that a solid has its own size and shape. **Are the things in this box solids, liquids, or gases?** (solids) **You can use a balance to measure the mass of a solid. What can you use to measure the size of a solid?** (a ruler)

Pages 244–245: **Liquids**
What kinds of things can you keep in these containers? (Possible responses: applesauce, syrup, honey, juice) Point out that these containers can hold different liquids. **Liquid is matter that does not have its own shape. When you pour a liquid into a container, it takes the shape of the container. Liquids take up space and have mass.** Point to the measuring cup. **This is used to measure the amount of space a liquid takes up. The space a liquid takes up is called volume.**

Pages 246–247: **Gases**
What is inside the bubble—a gas, a liquid, or a solid? (gas) Explain that gas is matter that takes the size and shape of its container. **Gas can change size and shape. It takes up all the space inside its container.** To reinforce understanding, ask: **How are liquids and gases similar? How are they different?** Point out that both liquids and gases take the shape of the container. However, gases also take the entire size of their containers.

Every Student Learns

Lesson 3: How can matter be changed?

Vocabulary

fold	tear	*mixture
mold	bend	

Activate Prior Knowledge/Build Background

Give each child a sheet of colored construction paper. **What does your paper look like?** (Possible answer: one piece, flat, straight sides, four corners) **Change this paper in any way or ways that you want.** After children have finished, call on volunteers to show their work and explain what they did to change the size and shape. **Can you change the color? How?**

Access Content

ᥱᥱᥱ Picture/Text Walk

Pages 248–249: **Ways to change matter**
Invite children to describe the different matter in the pictures and ways they were changed. **What do you change when you fold paper?** (its size, shape) **What do you change when you tear paper?** (its size, shape) **What happens when you mold clay?** (you change its shape) **What happens when you bend a pipe cleaner?** (you change its shape)

Pages 250–251: **Mixtures, separating mixtures**
Point to the picture of the fruit salad. **What is in the fruit salad?** Point out the fruit salad is a mixture of different fruits. **A mixture is made of two or more things that do not change. What happens if you separate the fruits in the salad? Do any of the fruits change?**

Page 251: Point to the pictures of the glasses. **These pictures show mixtures that are made with water. There are different ways to separate these mixtures. You can let the matter sink. You can let the water evaporate. How can you separate the sand and the water?** (let the sand sink) **How can you separate the salt and water?** (let the water evaporate)

Extend Language

Write the words *mix* and *separate* on the chalkboard. Say the words aloud. **These words have opposite meanings. When you *mix*, you put things together. When you *separate*, you take things apart.** Ask children to name other word pairs that have opposite meanings. Write children's responses on the chalkboard. As a class, discuss each word pair and how their meanings are opposite.

Lesson 4: How can cooling and heating change matter?

Activate Prior Knowledge/Build Background

Place an ice cube in a bowl and set the bowl under a lamp. Have students predict what will happen to the ice cube. Invite them to tell about their own experiences with frozen things melting. What kinds of things melt? (Possible answer: ice cream, frozen fruit juice treats) **Why do these things melt?** Elicit that warmer temperatures cause frozen liquids to melt.

Access Content

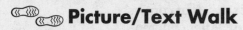 **Picture/Text Walk**

Pages 252–253: **Cooling water**
Point to the tray of liquid water. **Is this water a liquid or a solid? When the temperature of water is 0° Celsius or lower, the water will freeze.** Point to the tray of ice cubes. **This tray has been in the freezer, where the temperature is lower than 0° Celsius. What has happened to the water?** Elicit that it has become ice. **Is ice a liquid or a solid?** Point to the glass. **Water can change from a gas to a liquid. This glass is cold. Water vapor in the air touches the cold glass. The water vapor turns into drops of water on the glass.**

Pages 254–255: **Heating matter**
Point to the melting snow. **Heat can change solids to liquids. What is snow?** (solid water) **When snow melts, what does it change to?** (liquid water) **Where does the heat come from?** (the Sun) Point to the pot. **How can you change liquid water to a gas?** (heat it) Explain that heat can change other matter from solids to liquids. **What happens to wax when you burn a candle?** (the wax melts)

Extend Language

Talk about how the verb *freeze* changes form from present to past tense. The past tense of *freeze* is *froze*. Write these two sentences on the board: *Water freezes when it is very cold. The pond froze in December.* Help students write new sentences using the present and past tense of *freeze*.

Infer

Look at the picture. Write what you know. Then answer the question.

Infer Is it morning or noon?

I Know	I Can Infer
The shadow of the tree is _____. Shadows are long in _____.	→ It is morning.

Infer What is the weather like?

I Know	I Can Infer
_____ blows the leaves on the tree.	→ It is windy.

Lesson 1: What is energy?

Vocabulary

*energy	*solar energy

Activate Prior Knowledge/Build Background

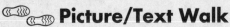 **Picture/Text Walk**

Pages 270–271: **Energy**
Point to the picture of the girls. **What are the girls doing? Are they using energy?** Explain that our bodies use energy all the time. When we do work or play, we use energy. Anything that can do work and make change has energy.

Pages 272–273: **Solar energy**
Explain that this house uses solar energy to stay warm. Solar energy is heat and light from the Sun. **What other things does the Sun warm? How do people and animals use sunlight in the daytime?**

Access Content

Ask students to name words to describe the Sun. **Is the Sun hot or cold? What happens when you leave something out in the Sun?** Explain that heat from the Sun warms the land, air, and water. This is solar energy. Earth gets most of its energy from the Sun.

Use two thermometers to show how sunlight warms the objects it touches. Leave both thermometers in a shaded place for 5 minutes. Have students record the temperature registered on each thermometer. Then, place one of the thermometers in direct sunlight for 5 minutes. Have students record the temperature on each thermometer again. Have students compare the temperature readings for each thermometer and discuss their observations.

Picture It! Infer

Explain that *infer* means to use what you know to answer a question. Discuss the picture of the tree. Ask children what they see in the picture. Is the shadow long or short? What is blowing the tree's leaves? Guide children as they fill in the blanks in the "I know" boxes. Help them to infer that in the first example it is morning. In the second example, they should infer that it is windy.

© Pearson Education, Inc. 2

Every Student Learns

Lesson 2: How do living things use energy?

Vocabulary

healthy	vitamins	nutrients
vegetables	minerals	

Activate Prior Knowledge/Build Background

Bring in a lunch that includes something from each of the five food groups. Make a five-column chart with the names of the five groups as column headers. As students identify each item, write its name in the correct food group. Then, ask students to name other types of food. Add them to the chart. List at least five items in each group.

Access Content

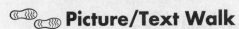 Picture/Text Walk

Pages 274–275: **Flowers, animal, girl eating, girls playing**
Living things need energy. Point to the flowers. **Plants use sunlight, air, and water to make food. Plants use the food to live and grow.** Point to the animal eating. **Where does this animal get energy? Animals get energy from the food they eat. They use energy to live and grow.** Point to the girl eating and the girls playing. **Where do these girls get energy?** Explain that people eat food that comes from plants or from animals that eat plants.

Pages 276–277: **Five food groups**
Food gives you energy. What do you need energy to do? Review the five food groups. Point to each photo and ask the children to identify each group. **You should eat foods from each group every day. Vegetables have vitamins your body needs. Meat, fish, eggs, and dry beans have nutrients that help your body grow. Fruit has many vitamins and minerals that can help you stay healthy. Milk, yogurt, and cheese help your bones and teeth stay healthy. What is the other food group?**

© Pearson Education, Inc. **2**

Lesson 3: What are some sources of heat?

Vocabulary

*source	*fuel	*conductor

Activate Prior Knowledge/Build Background

Have students draw a picture of something that creates heat. Ask them to draw a picture of the heat source and what it is warming. Then have students show their drawings and explain the heat source and what it is heating.

Access Content

Picture/Text Walk

Page 278: **Hands**
What do you do to warm your hands when they are cold? Ask a student to demonstrate. **You can rub your hands together to warm them.**

Page 278: **Candle**
A place that something comes from is called a source. Point out that sunlight is a source of heat that warms Earth. **What source of heat do you see in this picture?**

Page 279: **Campfire**
What source of heat do you see in this picture? Explain that fuel is something that we burn to make heat. **What fuel is burning in the campfire? Wood is a kind of fuel.** Explain that coal, gas, and oil are other kinds of fuel.

Page 280: **Frying pan**
What does this picture show? Explain that the heat moves from the stove burner to the pan to the cold food. **Heat moves from warm things to cool things. A conductor is something that lets heat move through it easily. This pan is metal. Is metal a good conductor? The cooking mitt is made of cloth. Is cloth a good conductor?**

Page 281: **Water boiling**
What does this picture show? How do you heat water? Explain that the pot and the water are cool. **If you put the pot on the stove, the heat moves from the stove to the pot. What will happen to the water when the pot gets hot? Is the pot a good conductor?**

Every Student Learns

Lesson 4: How does light move?

Vocabulary

*reflects	shiny
straight	*shadow

Activate Prior Knowledge/Build Background

Provide students with a flashlight, a clear jar filled with water, and a mirror. Have small groups of students take turns shining the flashlight directly at objects, at the mirror, and through the jar of water. Discuss with students how light moves in straight lines, how water bends light, and how the mirror reflects light.

Access Content

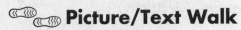 **Picture/Text Walk**

Page 282: **Flashlight**
Explain that light is a form of energy. **What are some sources of light?** Explain that light moves in straight lines. Light reflects when it bounces off of something. **Light reflects well from smooth, shiny things, such as a mirror.**

Page 283: **Rainbow**
Point to the rainbow. **What is this? When do you see a rainbow? White light has many colors in it. Raindrops in the air can bend sunlight. Then the sunlight is separated into the colors of the rainbow. What are the colors in a rainbow?**

Pages 284–285: **Changing shadows**
Explain that when something is in the way of light, it makes a shadow. Point to the two pictures on page 284. **Are shadows long or short in the morning?** (long) **At noon?** (short) **At sunset?** (long)

Extend Language

Review meanings of the word *light*. The noun *light* can mean either "a form of energy" or "a source of light." The adjective *light* can mean either "not heavy" or "not dark." Write these sentences: *There is a lot of light here. Please turn off the light. My bag is light blue. The empty box is light.* Have students explain the meaning of *light* in each sentence. Then ask them to create new sentences with *light*.

Lesson 5: What are other kinds of energy?

Vocabulary

motion	sound	safely
wind	electricity	

Activate Prior Knowledge/Build Background

Remind students that anything that can do work or make a change happen has energy. Make a two-column chart with two subheadings *Kind of Energy* and *What It Can Do*. **What kinds of energy have we learned about?** Fill in the chart as students name different kinds of energy (solar energy, heat, light) and what they can do (warm land, cook food, let people see). Ask students what kind of energy a computer uses. (electricity)

Access Content

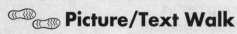 **Picture/Text Walk**

Pages 286–287: **Sailboat, instruments, shopping cart**
Point at each picture. **There are many kinds of energy. What energy makes the sailboat move? Wind is a kind of energy. These instruments make sound. Sound is a kind of energy. How does the shopping cart move? How does it get energy? When you push something, it has the energy of motion. Motion is when something moves.**

Pages 288–289: **Toy car, clock, lamp**
What kind of energy makes these things work? Explain that electricity is a kind of energy. **When you turn on a light, electricity makes the light work. What other things use electricity? People can store electricity in batteries. What things use batteries?**
Review the *Electricity Safety Tips* on page 289 with students.

© Pearson Education, Inc. **2**

🎯 Put Things in Order

Look at the pictures. Write 1, 2, or 3 in the small corner box to put the pictures in order so they tell what happened first, next, and last. Use the story to help you.

First, Mari needs help with the swing.
Next, her brother gives her a push.
Last, Mari goes high up on the swing.

Now, look at these pictures and read the story. Write the numbers 1, 2, or 3 in the small corner box to put the pictures in order. Fill in the blanks.

_____, Jenny is going to finish her birdhouse.

_____, she hits the last nail with the hammer.

_____, now the birdhouse is finished.

Lesson 1: How do objects move?

Vocabulary

*motion	pull	*gravity
push	*force	

Activate Prior Knowledge/Build Background

Bring a toy car or truck to class. Invite a volunteer to push it across the floor. Explain that motion is the act of moving; things can move in different ways. **How did the truck move?** (in a straight line) Move the truck in a zigzag motion. **How is the truck moving now?**

Access Content

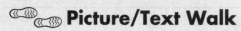 Picture/Text Walk

Page 304: **Pushing and pulling**
Give the truck another push. **What am I doing to make the truck move?** Explain that a push or pull that makes something move is called a force; a force changes the way something moves. Point to the picture on page 304. **What are the children doing?** (pulling a rope) **Which way will the rope move?** Discuss how an object will move in the direction it is pushed or pulled.

Page 307: **Basketball**
Encourage a volunteer to jump into the air. **What happened to Angela** (the volunteer's name) **after she jumped into the air?** (She was pulled down to Earth.) **What caused Angela to come back down?** Point to the picture on page 307. Ask children to trace the movement of the basketball with their fingers. **What happened to the basketball after it was thrown into the air?** Explain that gravity is a force; it pulls things down to Earth.

Picture It! Put Things in Order

Point out to children that when you put things in order you tell what happens first, next, and last. Tell children that the pictures are in the wrong order. Read the story aloud. Guide children as they write the order the pictures should be in. Then have children look at the second row of pictures and read the story. Help them as needed as they write the order the pictures should be in.

Every Student Learns

Lesson 2: What is work?

Vocabulary

*work

Activate Prior Knowledge/Build Background

Give each child a block. Ask children to move their blocks and explain
how they did so. Remind children that they used force to move their
blocks. Explain that by making their blocks move, children did work.

Access Content

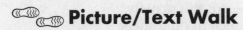 **Picture/Text Walk**

Pages 308–309: **Bobsled team and rock**
Push a crayon across a desk. **Am I doing work?** Point to the bobsled
team in the picture. **What are they doing? Are they doing work?**
Does it take more work to move the crayon or to move the
bobsled? Explain that it takes more force to move something heavy than
to move something light.

Remind children that in order for work to happen, an object must move.
Point to the picture of the people pulling the rock. **These people cannot**
make the rock move. Are they doing work?

© Pearson Education, Inc. 2

Lesson 3: How can you change the way things move?

Vocabulary

*friction	farther
far	farthest

Activate Prior Knowledge/Build Background

Give pairs of children two pennies and a ruler. On a smooth surface, instruct children to tap the second penny lightly; it should slide easily. Then, have children tap the penny so it slides farther. Repeat this activity, having children slide the pennies on a rougher surface, such as on a sheet of paper or on a carpet. **Did the pennies slide better on one surface than another?** Discuss how pushing the pennies on the rougher surface required more force.

Access Content

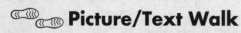 **Picture/Text Walk**

Pages 310–311: **Kicking the soccer ball**
Point to the picture on page 310 and say, **This soccer player is tapping the ball. Is she using a lot of force?** (no) **Will the ball move far?** (no) Point to the picture on page 311 and say **This soccer player is using a lot of force to kick the ball. Will the ball move far?** (yes) Explain that it takes more work to move the soccer ball farther.

Pages 312–313: **Road and grass**
Remind children of their penny experiment at the beginning of the lesson. Then, point to the pictures. **Look at these pictures. Do you think a bicycle moves faster on a smooth road or on grass?** (road) Explain that friction is a force that makes moving things slow down or stop moving; the friction between the wheels and the grass slowed the movement of the bicycle.

Extend Language

Review the adverbs *far*, *farther*, and *farthest*. *Far* is used to describe the distance an object moves. *Farther* is used to compare two distances. *Farthest* describes a distance that is longer than all others. Mimic the penny activity at the top of the page. Use three pennies. Guide the class to use *far*, *farther*, *farthest* to describe the distance each penny has moved.

© Pearson Education, Inc. 2

Every Student Learns

Lesson 4: How can simple machines help you do work?

Vocabulary

tool	screw	wheel and axle
*simple machine	lever	pulley
wedge	inclined plane	

Activate Prior Knowledge/Build Background

Bring a screwdriver to class. Hold it up for children to see. **Is this a machine?** (yes) Explain that a machine is a tool that can do work. A machine can make work easier. **A screwdriver is a simple machine. It doesn't have many parts.** Make a list of machines, both simple and complex. Help children to identify and circle the simple machines listed.

Access Content

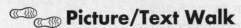 **Picture/Text Walk**

Pages 314–315: **Six simple machines**
Point to and name each machine pictured: wedge, screw, lever, wheel and axle, inclined plane, pulley. Describe what each simple machine can do.

Pages 316–317: **Animals and machines**
Some animals have body parts that are like simple machines. These body parts help animals do work. Encourage children to identify each animal. Point to the body parts that work as simple machines. Discuss how these body parts are similar to the simple machines shown. Discuss the work each body part can do.

Extend Language

Point to and read the first caption on page 316. Discuss how the word *like* is used to compare an animal's body part to a simple machine. Read the other caption on page 316 and the captions on page 317. Encourage children to raise their hands when they hear the word *like*. Invite volunteers to identify the two objects that were compared.

Lesson 5: What are magnets?

Vocabulary

magnet	*repel	opposite
*attract	poles	metal

Activate Prior Knowledge/Build Background

Before the class, lay out a variety of items, such as paper clips, an eraser, a penny, a nickel, and a pencil. Hold up a magnet for children to see. **What is this?** Demonstrate how the magnet attracts the paper clips. Ask children to guess which other items the magnet will attract. Then, call on volunteers to choose one item and test it with the magnet.

Access Content

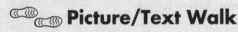 **Picture/Text Walk**

Page 319: **Magnets**
A magnet has a north pole and a south pole. Point to the first set of magnets. Invite volunteers to identify both poles on each magnet. Use two magnets to demonstrate as you say, **Magnets repel if you put two poles that are alike together. *Repel* means to push away.** Point to the second set of magnets. **Magnets attract if you put opposite poles together. *Attract* means to pull toward.**

Pages 320–321: **Magnets and metals**
Point to the magnet and the objects it has attracted on page 320. Explain that magnets attract some metal objects. Point to the other objects. **Why didn't the magnet attract these items?**

Extend Language

Review the meanings of *attract* and *repel.* Write *N* on five index cards; write *S* on five index cards. Give each pair of children a set of ten index cards. Instruct children to mix the cards and stack them in a pile. The letters *N* and *S* should be facing down. Children should alternate turning over the top two cards and placing them faceup. Pairs should call out *Repel!* if the cards show the same letter and *Attract!* if the cards show different letters.

Every Student Learns

Important Details

Look at the pictures. Read the words.

whale   drum tuba   cricket   bird   violin

Things That Make   Things That Make
Low Pitch Sounds   High Pitch Sounds

What things make a high pitch sound?

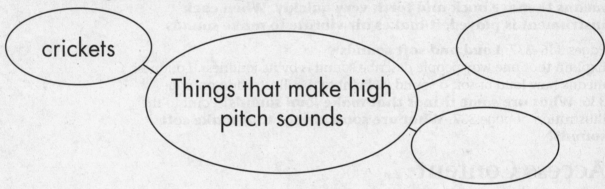

crickets

Things that make high
pitch sounds

What things make a low pitch sound?

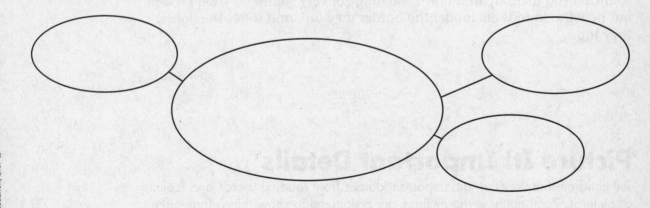

Lesson 1: What is sound?

Vocabulary

instruments	*vibrate	soft
sound	*loudness	

Activate Prior Knowledge/Build Background

Picture/Text Walk

Pages 334–335: **Marching band**
What instruments are these people playing? (trombones, trumpets, saxophones, flutes) Point out that each instrument makes a different sound. Explain that sound is made when something vibrates. **Vibrate means to move back and forth very quickly. When each instrument is played, it makes air vibrate to make sounds.**

Pages 336–337: **Loud and soft sounds**
Explain that one way people describe sound is by its loudness. Loudness means how loud or soft a sound is. Point to the illustration on page 336. **What are some things that make loud sounds?** Point to the illustration of page 337. **What are some things that make soft sounds?**

Access Content

Provide small groups of students with empty cans. Explain to students that they are going to make soft and loud sounds by tapping on the cans with their pencils. You will indicate how softly or loudly they should play by saying *softer* or *louder*. Start by telling students to start making soft sounds. Lead them up and down the range of very soft to very loud. Point out how the sounds get louder the harder they tap, and softer the lighter they tap.

Picture It! Important Details

Tell children that they can get important details from reading words and looking at pictures. Point out how the pictures are organized to show things that make low pitch sounds and high pitch sounds. Guide them to complete the graphic organizer for things that make a high pitch sound. Then help children fill in the graphic organizer for things that make a low pitch sound. Point out that they need to write what the organizer describes in the center oval.

© Pearson Education, Inc. 2

Lesson 2: What is pitch?

Vocabulary

*pitch

Activate Prior Knowledge/Build Background

Bring in three bottles with narrow necks and a pitcher of water. Invite three students to each blow across the tops of the empty bottles. Fill the first bottle one-third full, stopping at intervals to let the student blow across the top. Then repeat with the second bottle, filling it two-thirds full, and the third bottle, filling it nearly to the top. Discuss with students what they observed about the sounds.

Access Content

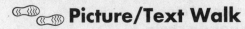 **Picture/Text Walk**

Pages 338–339: **Glass bottles**
Explain that another way to describe sound is by its pitch. Pitch means how high or low a sound is. **Things that vibrate quickly make a sound with a high pitch. What kind of sound do things that vibrate slowly make?** (sound with a low pitch) Point to the bottles. Explain that when you blow across a bottle, the air inside vibrates. **Bottles with a lot of air make sounds with a low pitch. What kind of sound do bottles with a little air make?** (sounds with a high pitch)

Page 339: **Animals sounds**
Point to the picture of the bird. **Have you ever heard a bird make sounds? Did the sounds have a high or a low pitch?** (sounds with a high pitch) Point to the bullfrog. **What kind of sounds does the bullfrog make?** (sounds with a low pitch)

Extend language

Remind students that sounds have *loudness* and *pitch*. Write *loud* and *soft* on two index cards and *high pitch* and *low pitch* on two more index cards. Practice these words for loudness and pitch by picking one card from each group and holding them up for students to see. Tell students to make a sound that the two cards describe, for example, soft and high-pitched or loud and low-pitched.

Lesson 3: How does sound travel?

Activate Prior Knowledge/Build Background

Have children pair up and take turns tapping on a desktop with their finger. The other student should first listen to the tapping through the air, and then, by pressing one ear against the desktop. Ask students which sound was louder, the one they heard through the air or the sound they heard through the desktop. Ask children why they think one sound was louder than the other.

Access Content

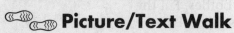 **Picture/Text Walk**

Pages 340–341: **Sound travels**
Ask children to name the different animals pictured. **Each of these animals can make sounds. Sounds move through solids, liquids, and gases.** Point to the lion. **The roar of a lion moves through the air.** Point to the woodpecker. **The woodpecker pecks at the tree. What does its sound move through?** (the air and the tree) Point to the dolphins. **Dophins make whistles and clicks. What do their sounds move through?** (the water) Explain to children that sound moves fast through gases, such as air. Sound moves faster through liquids, such as water, than it does through air. Sound moves fastest through solids such as wood or metal.

Lesson 4: How do some animals make sounds?

Activate Prior Knowledge/Build Background

Invite students to imitate the sounds that different animals make. Make a two-column list with the headings *Animal* and *Sound.* After students imitate the sound of an animal, ask them to say the name of the animal and write the name of the sound, for example, *roar* or *quack.*

Access Content

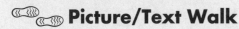 **Picture/Text Walk**

Pages 342–343: **Animal sounds**
Explain that animals make sounds in many ways. Point to the cricket. **A cricket makes sounds the way a guitar makes sounds. The cricket rubs one wing on the other wing. Then the other wing vibrates to make sound. It is like a guitar pick that makes a guitar string vibrate.** Point to the rattlesnake. **A rattlesnake makes sounds like maracas. The snake shakes the rattle in its tail.** Point to the lobster. **This lobster makes sounds like a violin. You play a violin by rubbing the bow against the strings. The lobster uses its antenna like a bow. It rubs its antenna against the side of its head.**

Extend language

Point out that *guitar, maracas,* and *violin* are all names of musical instruments. Make a list of names of musical instruments. Ask students for the names of instruments they saw at the beginning of the chapter. (trombone, trumpet, saxophone, flute) Brainstorm additional names of instruments. Then invite students to pantomime playing these different instruments and to imitate the sounds they make.

Lesson 5: What are some sounds around you?

Activate Prior Knowledge/Build Background

Ask students to be silent for two minutes and to listen carefully for any sound. Ask them to write down all the sounds they hear during the two minutes of silence. Then have students share their list with the class. What was the softest sound they heard? What was the loudest sound? Which had the highest pitch? Which had the lowest pitch?

Access Content

 Picture/Text Walk

Pages 344–345: **Busy city**
Ask children to identify the various activities in the picture and the kinds of sounds they make. Point out that there are sounds around us all the time. **What are some sounds that you hear in your neighborhood? What are the loudest sounds? What are the softest sounds? What sounds do you hear in the day? What sounds do you hear at night?**

Extend Language

List the following words in a column on the board: *clang, buzz, boom, squeak, gush, whirr, hush, wow, kerplunk,* and *splash.* Tell children that some words are spelled like the sound they describe. Say each word aloud. Ask children what kind of sound the word makes. Is it a loud or soft sound? Does it have a high or low pitch? Then ask children to name things that make that sound and where they might hear it. Write children's responses beside each word.

© Pearson Education, Inc. **2**

Name _____

Alike and Different

Compare constellations. Tell how the Big Dipper and the Little Dipper are the same and different.

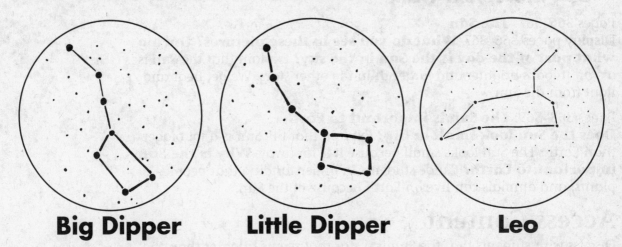

| **Big Dipper** | **Little Dipper** | **Leo** |

Alike	Different
They both have seven stars.	

Now tell how the Little Dipper and Leo are alike and different.

Alike	Different

Lesson 1: What is the Sun?

Activate Prior Knowledge/Build Background

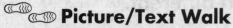 **Picture/Text Walk**

Pages 366–367: **The Sun**
Display pages 366–367. **What do you see in these pictures? During what part of the day is the Sun in the sky?** Explain that the Sun is a star. It looks brighter and larger than the other stars. We get heat and light from the Sun.

Pages 368–369: **The Sun is important to Earth**
Does the Sun look small or big? Explain that the Sun is a lot bigger than Earth. The Sun looks small because it is far away. **Why is the Sun important to Earth?** Guide students in understanding that people, plants, and animals can live on Earth because of the Sun.

Access Content

Discuss with students that the Sun is a star that seems brighter than the other stars because its closer to Earth. Tell them that all stars are made of hot, bright gases.

Picture It! Alike and Different

Have students look at the first two pictures to compare the Big and Little Dippers. Tell students that they can look at the shapes and the sizes of the constellations and how many stars are in each one. Guide them to complete the Alike and Different organizer comparing the Big and Little Dippers. (Possible answers: Different: The Little Dipper has a different shape.) Then have them compare the Little Dipper and Leo and complete the organizer. (Answers may include: Alike: They are groups of stars. Different: They have different shapes. They have a different number of stars in them.)

Lesson 2: What causes day and night?

Vocabulary

spinning	*rotation
*axis	face

Activate Prior Knowledge/Build Background

Provide students with a variety of tops. Ask them to take turns spinning the tops. Point out that each top spins around its center. Explain that an imaginary line through the center of each top is called its axis. Each top spins on its axis. Have them draw a picture of each top and then draw a line to show its axis.

Access Content

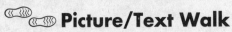 **Picture/Text Walk**

Pages 370–371: **Earth's axis**
This is a picture of Earth. What is it doing? (spinning) **What is the imaginary line through the center of Earth called?** (axis) **Spinning on an axis is called a rotation. Earth makes one complete rotation every day.** Explain that Earth's rotation causes day and night. **When the side of Earth where you live faces the Sun, you have daytime. What do you have when your side of Earth faces away from the Sun?** (night)

Pages 372–373: **The movement of the Sun**
Which picture shows the sky in the morning? How do you know? (The Sun is low in the sky; *sunrise*) **Which picture shows the middle of the day? How do you know?** (The Sun is high in the sky; *noon*) **Which picture shows the evening? How do you know?** (The Sun is low in the sky; *sunset*) Explain that even though it looks as if the Sun moves across the sky, it does not. The Earth is moving.

Extend Language

Remind students that there are many words that begin with *sun*. Write *sunrise, sunset, sunlight, sunny,* and *Sunday*. Review the meaning of each word. Then have students make sentences that use each of these words. Invite them to create sentences that use two or three of these words.

Lesson 3: What causes seasons to change?

Vocabulary

*orbit	tilted

Activate Prior Knowledge/Build Background

Insert a yard-long length of string through a small rubber ball. Put a knot in the string once it has gone through the ball to secure the ball. Slowly swing the ball around over your head. Guide students in describing the movement of the ball and to say what the ball is moving around in a kind of circle. Explain that the ball represents Earth and you represent the Sun that Earth moves around.

Access Content

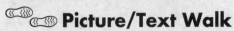 Picture/Text Walk

Pages 374–375: **Earth's orbit**
Point to the picture. **You have learned that Earth spins on its axis. Earth also moves around the Sun in an orbit. An orbit is a path around another object.** Trace the path of Earth's orbit with your finger. **Earth takes about one year to orbit the Sun.** Point to the different pictures of Earth. **Is Earth's axis straight or tilted to one side?** (tilted) **The tilt of Earth and Earth's orbit around the Sun make the seasons change.** Point to Earth's position in winter. **In winter, the part of Earth where we live is tilted away from the Sun. What season is it when the part of Earth where we live is tilted toward the Sun?** (summer)

Extend Language

Review the words *axis, rotation,* and *orbit*. Have pairs of students act out the rotating Earth orbiting the Sun. Have a volunteer be the Sun and give another student a ball to represent Earth. Have the student with the ball rotate Earth as he or she walks around the Sun to represent Earth's orbit. Ask the student playing the Sun to point out the axis, rotation, and orbit of Earth.

Lesson 4: What can you see in the night sky?

Vocabulary

---

*constellation   *crater

Activate Prior Knowledge/Build Background

Use a picture of constellations to draw Orion and the Big Dipper on the board. Below each constellation, draw the pattern of stars for that constellation without the connecting lines. Have students take turns connecting the stars to form the constellations. Invite students to draw or name other constellations they know.

Access Content

 Picture/Text Walk

Pages 376–377: **Constellations**
The Sun is a star you can see in the daytime. What can you see in the sky at night? (stars, the Moon) Explain that long ago, people imagined that some stars formed pictures. Show how a group of stars can form a picture called a constellation. **What does Leo look like to you? What do the Big Dipper and the Little Dipper look like?**

Pages 378–379: **The Moon**
What is the biggest and brightest object in the sky at night? (the Moon) Ask students to look at the close-up of the Moon. **What landforms can you see?** (They may recognize raised landforms and large holes.) Point out that the Moon has mountains and craters. Explain that a crater is a hole in the ground that has the shape of a bowl. **When a big rock from space hits the Moon, it makes a crater.** Point to the picture showing the Moon in daytime. **Sometimes you can see the Moon in the daytime. Have you ever seen the Moon during the day?**

Extend Language

Write the following sentence on the board: *The moon looks like a big balloon.* Read the sentence aloud. Ask which two words end with the same sounds. (moon/balloon) Tell children that words that end with the same sounds are rhyming words. Write the following words on the board: *soon, noon, spoon, June, tune.* Read the words aloud as a class. Point out that all these words also rhyme with *Moon.* Invite children to create their own sentences using words that rhyme with *Moon.*

Lesson 5: Why does the Moon seem to change?

Vocabulary

*phase

Activate Prior Knowledge/Build Background

Invite students to tell what they know about the Moon, including factual information, sayings, and stories or legends. Ask what they see when they look at the full Moon. Invite them to offer explanations for why the Moon changes its shape.

Access Content

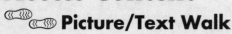 Picture/Text Walk

Pages 380–381: **The phases of the Moon**
Explain that the Moon rotates like Earth. But the Moon moves in an orbit around Earth. **The Moon moves around Earth. What does Earth move around?** (the Sun) **It takes about four weeks for the Moon to move one time around Earth.** Point to the photos of the Moon. **The Moon does not make light. The Moon reflects light from the Sun. You only see the part of the Moon that has sunlight on it. This is called a phase.** Explain to students that as the Moon moves around Earth, the amount of light reflected from the Sun changes. Point out that on some nights the Moon looks round. On other nights the Moon looks smaller. Sometimes you cannot see the Moon. The shape of the part of the Moon that reflects light is called a phase.

Every Student Learns

Lesson 6: What is the solar system?

Vocabulary

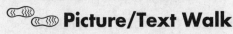

*solar system

Activate Prior Knowledge/Build Background

Show students pictures of each of the planets. Have them tell the class what they know about the different planets. Then ask them to talk about imaginary planets they have read about or seen in movies. **Are those planets like any of the real planets?** Display pictures of planets and the solar system around the room.

Access Content

Picture/Text Walk

Pages 382–383: **The solar system**
What is Earth? (a planet) **What does Earth orbit?** (the Sun) Point to the illustration of the solar system. **Other planets orbit the Sun too. The planets, the moons of the planets, and everything else that moves around the Sun is called the solar system. What is the center of the solar system?** (the Sun) **How many planets move around the Sun?** (nine) Invite students to point out individual planets and say the names of them together.

Retell

They Made It First!

Read the story.

George Crum invented potato chips in 1853. George Crum was a cook. One man did not like his French fries. The man said they were too thick. George Crum then cut the potatoes in very thin slices. The man loved the potato chips George Crum made.

Retell what you learned about potato chips.

Retell

George Crum invented _____.

A man thought _____ were too thick.

So George Crum _____

_____.

The man loved George Crum's _____.

© Pearson Education, Inc. **2**

Lesson 1: What is technology?

Vocabulary

*technology	*transportation	gasoline
*invent	*engine	

Activate Prior Knowledge/Build Background

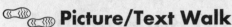 **Picture/Text Walk**

Pages 398–399: **The modern car**
What do people use to travel long distances? (cars, airplanes) **What do people use to talk to each other?** (phones, cell phones) **What do people use to write to each other?** (mail, computers) Explain that cars, airplanes, telephones, and computers use *technology.* Technology means using science to solve problems. People can use technology to invent things. *Invent* means to make something for the first time.

Pages 400–401: **Forms of transportation**
Explain that technology has changed transportation. Transportation is the way people or things move from one place to another place. **An engine is a machine that does work or makes something move.** Point to the covered wagon. **Does a covered wagon have an engine?** Point to the train. **Long ago, steam engines made trains and boats move. Today, cars, trains, and boats have gasoline or electric engines.** Point to the airplane. **What do we use to travel through the air? Through space?**

Access Content

Have small groups of children brainstorm two lists, one of *Old* technology that they use or know about and the other of *New* technology that they use. Give the wheel and a pencil as examples of old technology and a computer and a CD player as examples of new technology. Then ask the groups to share their lists with the class.

Picture It! Retell

Read the story aloud and have children follow. Afterwards, ask children to verbally retell what the story is about. Point out that *retell* means to use your own words to tell what you have learned. Guide children to complete the paragraph to retell what they have learned about George Crum.

Lesson 2: How does technology help us?

Vocabulary

*vaccine	disease
medicine	artificial

Activate Prior Knowledge/Build Background

Ask children to name different ways to stay healthy. Then ask them to name sicknesses they have had or know about. Finally, ask children what a doctor can do to help a person with each sickness mentioned. Invite children to talk about the different kinds of technology they have seen doctors use.

Access Content

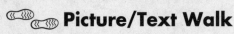 **Picture/Text Walk**

Page 402: **X ray and stethoscope**
Point to the doctor talking to the child. **What is the doctor holding?** (an X ray) **What does an X ray show?** (a person's insides) Brainstorm why doctors X ray patients. (to see if a patient is healthy, to see where a person is injured) Focus childrens' attention on the stethoscope around the doctor's neck. Explain that doctors use a stethoscope to listen to people's heartbeat and lungs.

Page 402: **Vaccine**
Point to the picture of the vaccine. **Doctors use vaccines to keep people from getting sick. A vaccine is a medicine that can keep people from getting a disease.**

Page 403: **Artificial leg**
Point to the picture of the man with the artificial leg. **What has happened to one of the man's real legs?** (He lost it.) **How does an artificial leg help him?** (He can walk and run with it.) **How would his life be different if he did not have an artificial leg?** (He would not be able to run and walk by himself.)

Extend language

Write the letter *x* and the word *x ray* on the board. Explain to children that the scientist who discovered X rays did not understand what the rays were, so he called them *x*. Explain that an X ray is a powerful ray of light that can go through things that normal rays of light cannot. Doctors use X rays to take pictures of bones and organs inside the body.

Lesson 3: How do we use technology to communicate?

Activate Prior Knowledge/Build Background

Discuss with children how people communicate. Make a two-column chart with the title *Communication* and the headings *Old Ways* and *New Ways*. Ask them to think of ways that people have communicated for a long time. Put these in the first column. Then have children think of new ways people communicate. Put these in the second column. (Old ways might include smoke signals, drumming, telephones, letters, and telegrams. New ways might include cell phones, e-mail, and faxes.)

Access Content

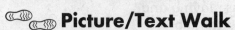 **Picture/Text Walk**

Page 404: **Telephones**
Use the pictures to discuss how telephones have changed over time. Point to the old telephone. **The first telephones hung on a wall.** Discuss the different parts of the old phone: bell, mouthpiece, hearing piece. **Compare the old telephone with the new telephone. How has the telephone changed?** (New telephones are small and light. You can carry a telephone with you.)

Page 405: **Computers**
Use the pictures to discuss how computers have changed over time. **How big was the first computer?** (as big as a room) **Only a few big companies used the early computers. How has the size of computers changed?** (they have become much smaller and fit on a desktop) **Who uses computers now?** Point out to children how technology has changed the ways people communicate. **What are some ways you use technology to communicate with your friends?**

Extend Language

Remind children that people use technology such as a telephone to communicate. Write the word *telephone* and its parts, *tele* and *phone*, on the board. Explain that, in Ancient Greek, an old language, *tele* means "distance" and *phone* means "sound." Point out that a telephone is something that sends and receives sound over a distance. Write *telescope* and *scope*. Explain that *scope* means "see" in Ancient Greek. Ask children what they think the meaning of the word *telescope* is.

Lesson 4: What are some other ways we use technology?

Vocabulary

*meteorologist   *satellite

Activate Prior Knowledge/Build Background

Brainstorm ways children have fun. **What are some things you do to relax? What are some ways that you entertain yourself?** List childrens' responses on the board. Elicit activities such as playing and listening to music, watching television, going to movies, riding bikes, and so on. Review the list with the class. **Did people long ago do these things to have fun? Which things didn't they do?** Call on volunteers to circle the activities that involve using technology. Point out that people use technology in many different ways, including having fun.

Access Content

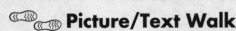 Picture/Text Walk

Page 406: **Electric guitar and MP3 player**
Point to each picture and discuss how people use them. **This is an electric guitar. Do all guitars use electricity?** Explain to children that even guitars that do not use electricity are examples of technology. They were invented to make sounds. **What other instruments can you name?** Point out that the MP3 player plays music from the Internet. **What are some ways that you use the Internet? In what ways is it helpful? In what ways do you use it for fun?**

Pages 407: **Meteorologist**
How do people find out about the weather? (Children may mention weather forecasts in the newspaper, on television, on the Internet.) Point to the meteorologist. **Technology helps people in their jobs. A meteorologist is a person who studies weather. Meteorologists use satellites to find out about the weather.** Point to the satellite. **A satellite is an object that moves around another object. Satellites in space send pictures of weather back to Earth.** Point to the meteorologist. **How does this meteorologist use pictures from a satellite?**

Lesson 5: How do people make things?

Vocabulary

*manufacture	materials

Activate Prior Knowledge/Build Background

Ask children to name all the materials that they are wearing. Remind them to look at their clothes, their shoes, and anything they are wearing on their wrists, fingers, neck, and hair. Record their responses in a three-column chart with the headings *Object, Material,* and *Natural or Human-made.* Discuss the results.

Access Content

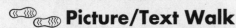 **Picture/Text Walk**

Pages 408–409: **Natural materials**
Point to the coat and to the bicycle. **People manufacture coats and bicycles. *Manufacture* means to make by hand or by machine.** Explain that some materials people use to make things are natural. That means they come from nature, such as plants and animals. Point to the coat. **This coat was made from wool. Where does wool come from?** (sheep) **The buttons are made of wood. Where does wood come from?** (trees)

Pages 408–409: **Human-made materials**
Point to the bicycle. Explain to children that some materials people use to make things are made by people. **All the parts of the bicycle are made by people. What are some of the parts that make up the bicycle?** (tires, seat, wheels, frame, handlebars) **What different materials make up the bike?** (plastic, metal, rubber)